(Giraudoux   )   129436

The Enchanted

A COMEDY

by Jean Giraudoux

Adapted by Maurice Valency

SAMUEL FRENCH
25 WEST 45TH ST.   NEW YORK 19
7623 SUNSET BLVD. HOLLYWOOD 46
LONDON   TORONTO

THE ENCHANTED

THE ENCHANTED
STORY OF THE PLAY

(9 Males; 11 Females)

It is the biography of a critical moment in the life of a young girl—the moment when she turns from girlhood to womanhood. In this moment, Isabel's belief in the life of the spirit is so strong that it is sufficient to evoke a real phantom, and even to threaten this world with a spiritual revolution. But where the Inspector, who represents the powers of Government and Science, is powerless against Isabel, the Eligible Young Man succeeds, and for Isabel, as for all young girls, the adventure of love proves more attractive in the end than the adventure of death.

THE ENCHANTED

Comedy by Jean Giraudoux; adapted by Maurice Valency; staged by George S. Kaufman; scenery by Robert Edmond Jones; music by Francis Poulence; dances by Jean Erdman; presented by David Lowe and Richard Davidson at the Lyceum Theatre, January 18, 1950. The cast:

THE MAYOR	*Charles Halton*
THE DOCTOR	*Russell Collins*
ISABEL	*Leueen MacGrath*
THE LITTLE GIRLS:	
GILBERTE	*Carolyn Grier*
DAISY	*Judith Licata*
LUCY	*Mimi Strongin*
VIOLA	*Leah Chernin*
DENISE	*Patricia Wright*
IRENE	*Betty Richardson*
MARIE-LOUISE	*Henrietta Catal*
THE INSPECTOR	*Malcolm Keen*
THE SUPERVISOR	*Wesley Addy*
ARMANDE MANGEBOIS	*Frances Williams*
LEONIDE MANGEBOIS	*Una O'Connor*
THE GHOST	*John Baragrey*
1ST EXECUTIONER	*Joe E. Marks*
2ND EXECUTIONER	*James O'Neill*
MONSIEUR ADRIAN	*John O'Hare*
PAPA TELLIER	*Roland Wood*

SNYOPSIS

ACT ONE

A clearing in the woods just outside a provincial town in France. Late afternoon.

ACT TWO

Th same. A few weeks later.

ACT THREE

Isabel's room in the town.

The Enchanted

ACT ONE

SCENE: *A beautiful green clearing in the woods, bordering a lake just outside a provincial town in France. The field is very open, but in one spot weeds have overgrown the ruins of what might have been a summer house. For the rest, the scene is innocence itself.*

> *There is a fallen log and bench at Left; a tree stump at Right.*

> *It is late afternoon in spring.*

AT RISE: *The stage is empty. Offstage Right, we hear a shout. Then the* MAYOR *enters Right, evidently in some trepidation.*

MAYOR. *(To Right Center)* Hello! *(There is no answer. Crosses Left Center and looks off Left)* Strange. Not even an echo.—Hello!

THE ECHO. Hello! *(The* MAYOR *turns in fear. The* DOCTOR *enters Right to down by stump.)*

DOCTOR. Hello, Mr. Mayor.

MAYOR. *(Crossing to* DOCTOR*)* Oh! It's you, Doctor?

DOCTOR. Did you think it was he?

MAYOR. Don't joke about it, please. We all know he doesn't exist—most likely. *(A step Left)* All the same, there's something queer about this place.

DOCTOR. This is the spot where he appears, eh?

MAYOR. Now don't let's be silly.

DOCTOR. But I thought you said—

5

MAYOR. I said this is where he is supposed to appear. It's nothing but an hallucination, of course. We all know that.

DOCTOR. If it's nothing but an hallucination, we could have met just as well in your office in the Town Hall.

MAYOR. Of course it's an hallucination.

DOCTOR. Then what, may I ask, made you choose this place for our meeting?

MAYOR. I didn't.

DOCTOR. No? Who did?

MAYOR. *(Crossing to* DOCTOR) The Inspector. Why? Do you feel a little nervous?

DOCTOR. Not a bit. *(Looks around)* To me, this spot looks as green and innocent as a golf course.

MAYOR. They never haunt a golf course?

DOCTOR. Very seldom. Nothing is further from the eternal than a golf course. *(Crosses up Right.)*

MAYOR. Really?

DOCTOR. A golf course is the epitome of all that is purely transitory in the universe, a space not to dwell in, but to get over as quickly as possible. In a golf course everything is calculated, limited and foreseen —even the hazards. Every blade of grass is registered —even the weeds.

MAYOR. This place is full of weeds.

DOCTOR. You're right. *(Going around stump down Right)* Well—! This place is by no means as innocent as it looks. There are all sorts of malignant things growing here—hellebore—and henbane—and even— yes, by God—! mandrake—! *(Above stump.)*

MAYOR. *(Crossing to* DOCTOR) You think it's true what they say about the mandrake?

DOCTOR. With regard to constipation?

MAYOR. With regard to demonology. They say, when a mandrake is impregnated with the seed of a hanged man, the child grows up to be a fiend. Can you believe that?

DOCTOR. It's quite possible. *(Crosses Left to log.)*

MAYOR. You don't suppose that this—apparition—is a thing of that sort?

DOCTOR. What does it look like? Dwarfish? Crooked? Black?

MAYOR. No. Tall. Young. Handsome.

DOCTOR. Have there been any hangings in the district?

MAYOR. During my term as Mayor, only one. The grocer's wife, you may remember the case. In the time of the ration cards. But she hanged herself by the feet, and only sprained her ankle.

DOCTOR. That won't do. It has to be a man, and with the feet down. I'm beginning to think our colleagues are lost. *(Crosses up Left.)*

MAYOR. *(Sits on stump)* No fear of that. I've asked the Supervisor of Weights and Measures to meet the Inspector at the station. The Supervisor knows exactly where we are.

DOCTOR. *(To down Left)* In my opinion, a committee of three would have been ample.

MAYOR. But the Supervisor is such a pleasant chap. There's a lad who doesn't know the meaning of fear. Did you hear what he did last night at the dinner? With a single phrase, imagine, he completely rehabilitated Catherine the Great! And in the very beard of the Fire Captain!

DOCTOR. I wasn't talking about the Supervisor.

MAYOR. He considers himself the local champion of the weaker sex. If anyone so much as opens his mouth—

DOCTOR. I meant the Inspector. Couldn't we have done without him?

MAYOR. *(Rising)* The Inspector? Oh, impossible. The Inspector insists on investigating in person all cases of subversive activity.

DOCTOR. And what gives him the idea that this ghost is subversive?

MAYOR. The Inspector considers everyone guilty

until he's proved innocent. You've heard of his latest inquiry?

DOCTOR. You mean those water nymphs at Limoges?

MAYOR. After three weeks of fact-finding, he decided to pave over the brook where they lived. The army engineers did the job. Nobody's seen any water nymphs since. Then there was the case of the pretty bay mare that was supposed to be making eyes at young men—

DOCTOR. He considered her subversive?

MAYOR. He had special blinders made; the poor beast has to wear them even in her stall at night.

DOCTOR. And this is the man who is coming to investigate our ghost!

MAYOR. He should be here by now. You don't suppose they've got themselves lost?

DOCTOR. *(To below log)* We might give them a shout?

MAYOR. *(To Right Center)* No, no. Please. There's something unusual about the acoustics here.

DOCTOR. You think?

MAYOR. I wouldn't shout. You can't tell who might answer.

DOCTOR. Now who could possibly answer, besides the Supervisor and the Inspector? *(He shouts)* Hello!

(There is a chorus of shrill VOICES in answer.)

THE VOICES. Hello! Hello! Hello!
MAYOR. Good God! What's that?

(A bevy of little GIRLS comes in Left. And after them, ISABEL.)

THE GIRLS. *(Botanizing)* Is this it, Miss Isabel? Is this the one? Is this it, Miss Isabel? Is this it?

THE MAYOR. *(To Center)* Oh, Miss Isabel! What a start you gave us!

ISABEL. *(To above log)* Hello, Mr. Mayor.

THE GIRLS. Hello, Mr. Mayor! Hello, Mr. Mayor!

DOCTOR. Are you having a holiday, children?

THE GIRLS. No—we're in school.

DOCTOR. You are? Where is your teacher?

MAYOR. Their teacher is having a baby. Isabel is acting as substitute.

DOCTOR. Ah. And where is your classroom?

ISABEL. *(Crossing Right to above stump)* The spring is our classroom, Doctor.

MAYOR. It's a trifle irregular, using the spring for a classroom, I suppose. But there's nothing in the regulations against it, nothing specific at any rate.

DOCTOR. What are we studying today, children?

THE GIRLS. Botany. Botany.

ISABEL. Yes, we're collecting all sorts of fascinating things—monkshood and hellebore and henbane and foxglove— And now we're after the most interesting of all. I know exactly where it grows.

DOCTOR. Which one is that?

THE GIRLS. The mandrake! The mandrake!

(IRENE, MARIE-LOUISE, VIOLA *exit down Right.)*

ISABEL. This way, children. *(Exits Right.)*

LUCY. Oh! Oh! I see it!

DENISE. Over here! Over here! *(ALL go out*

GILBERTE. Is this it? Is this it? *botanizing*

DAISY. Is this it, Miss Isabel? *intently.)*

DOCTOR. *(Crossing Right, past stump)* Isn't it wonderful how these innocents can move among the powers of evil without the slightest suspicion or the slightest fear? What a charming girl!

MAYOR. *(A step in)* I wish the Mangebois sisters were of your opinion.

DOCTOR. *(Turns)* What have those witches to do with Isabel?

MAYOR. We'll soon find out. They have asked to appear at the inquest. It seems they are going to prefer charges.

DOCTOR. Charges against Isabel? Ridiculous! That girl is as clear as a mountain stream. What's more, she makes everything else clear. Whatever she touches. (CHILDREN *laugh off Right.* DOCTOR *looks off*) Look at her now, beating time with a thistle while her little pupils dance a figure around her. You see? All at once, we understand the need for thistles in this world, and even the need for little girls. Dear me—what lovely little creatures!

MAYOR. My dear Doctor—

(There is a RUSTLE in the bushes off Left.)

DOCTOR. Ah—here we are. The Inspector.

(The INSPECTOR *enters busily up Left. The* SUPER-VISOR *with him.)*

INSPECTOR. *(To Left Center)* I understand perfectly. You demand proofs. Perfectly reasonable. You want a clear proof that the spirit world does not exist. Very well. Do you wish me to give you a proof this very minute?

SUPERVISOR. *(To Right end of log)* I shouldn't presume to hurry an official of your rank, Inspector.

INSPECTOR. You will grant, no doubt, that if spirits exist, they are able to hear what I say?

SUPERVISOR. All but the deaf ones, yes.

INSPECTOR. Very well, then. Let them listen to this! *(He addresses the air in the manner of a high official)* Spirits! Shapes spun of air and white of egg!—You notice I don't mince words with them. Spirits, through me, humanity defies you to manifest your presence! I offer you a unique opportunity to build up your credit in the community. I am not asking you to do anything spectacular. You don't have to blow invisible trumpets or materialize a live parrot. It will be quite sufficient if at the count of three you are able to cause an ordinary sparrow to fly into the air. Ready? One.

Two. Three!—You see, gentlemen? Nothing whatever. *(His hat flies off into the air)* Phew! What a wind.

DOCTOR. But the leaves are hardly stirring.

INSPECTOR. You see what I mean? It's pitiful. Well? Do you still expect me to believe in spirits?

SUPERVISOR. *(Sits on log)* Perhaps the spirits don't believe in you.

MAYOR. And furthermore—perhaps the invocation was not sufficiently specific. After all, why should they bother?

INSPECTOR. Oh, I see. You wish me to invoke them by name? All right. Shall I call up Asphlaroth?

DOCTOR. No, please, Inspector. Let's not fool with Asphlaroth. One never knows where these jokes can end.

INSPECTOR. *(Chuckling)* Incredible superstition! And you a health officer! Now watch this.—Hear me, Asphlaroth! Here I stand—a human organism that defies you to demonstrate your celebrated powers! You are said to be a specialist in the possession of the human body. You don't have to possess my whole body. Just the merest part of my body. I will stretch out my arm. Make me snap my fingers against my will and I'll believe in you as much as you like. Ready, Asphlaroth? One. Two. Three! *(He sneezes)* Pardon me.

DOCTOR. Have you a cold, Inspector?

INSPECTOR. It's the pollen.

MAYOR. But there isn't any pollen.

INSPECTOR. *(Wiping his nose)* Yes. And that's all Asphlaroth amounts to. Well? Are you convinced? He's nothing at all.

DOCTOR. *(Crossing to INSPECTOR)* It's not that simple, Inspector. His timing may be different from yours.

INSPECTOR. What?

DOCTOR. May I ask how you got that scar on your nose?

INSPECTOR. This? A brick fell on it when I was five.

DOCTOR. You see? He answered your insult forty years before you made it. *(Turns and sits on stump.)*

INSPECTOR. In that case, he's less than nothing—he's a coward who attacks defenseless children. (MAYOR *crosses.)* Mr. Mayor, I must tell you in all seriousness, the Administration considers your report utterly ludicrous. Spirits don't exist. Consequently they don't haunt towns. Not in my district.

MAYOR. They haunt this town.

INSPECTOR. Let's not be childish, Mr. Mayor. We know what ghosts are. Ghosts are a mysterious clashing of pots and pans at midnight in an apartment where they want to get the tenants out in order to raise the rent. Ghosts are a walking bedsheet that frightens away the night watchman in a warehouse just before a burglary. That's what ghosts are. *(Goes up.)*

SUPERVISOR. Not in this town, Inspector.

INSPECTOR. No? And just how are you haunted in this town?

SUPERVISOR. *(Rising; crosses in)* We are haunted by an occult presence which is clearly bent on sapping the foundations of civilized society. I might add, incidently, that I find myself in complete sympathy with its aims—

INSPECTOR. Really! And by what means is this power sapping the foundations of civilized society?

SUPERVISOR. We don't know the means. But we know the result. Take, for example, the behavior of the animals. Formerly, when a man beat a dog, the dog would cringe and lick his hand. Now he bites it. It's the same with the children.

INSPECTOR. *(Coming down Center)* They bite their parents?

SUPERVISOR. When children are mistreated, instead of crying and begging pardon, they simply leave the house and refuse to return. As for the women—there is a true miracle!

INSPECTOR. They've stopped chattering?

SUPERVISOR. Within the last month, our most desperate domestic problems have suddenly been solved —in the simplest imaginable way. The women have quietly left their husbands and gone off with more attractive men.

INSPECTOR. Is this really true?

DOCTOR. In this community, it is no longer respectable to be unhappy.

INSPECTOR. Not respectable—! Why wasn't I informed of this before?

(SUPERVISOR *crosses Left and sits on log.*)

MAYOR. *(Crosses to* INSPECTOR) I will add a few details. In the civic lottery, last Sunday, for the first time in history, the big cash prize went to the neediest couple in town—and not as always to Monsieur Dumas, the millionaire. The motorcycle was won by the young captain of the football team, and not as usual by the Mother Superior of the convent. On Wednesday, two people were run over by a motor truck. Not, as you might expect, the youngest and healthiest of our citizens, but the oldest and most decrepit—who happened to be also the stingiest and most venomous. You see what is happening? For the first time in the memory of man, fortune is displaying some intelligence, and chance seems to know what it is about.

INSPECTOR. What you are describing, my friend, is the nullification of human liberty.

DOCTOR. While you're on the subject, Mr. Mayor, you might say a word about the census returns.

MAYOR. I must confess I haven't had the courage to send in the forms, Inspector.

INSPECTOR. Your constituents have been telling lies, have they?

MAYOR. Quite the contrary. They have been telling the truth in so outrageous a manner that it amounts to indecency. Under "Name of Spouse," they have put down the names of movie stars, heroines of romance, and even occasionally the name of an automobile or a boat.

INSPECTOR. They're mad.

MAYOR. And under Section Two, instead of naming their children, many of them insist on putting down the names of dogs, cats, birds and even rubber plants —the things they really love and consider part of themselves.

INSPECTOR. That's punishable by fine and imprisonment.

MAYOR. Under the housing section, we find some of our richest and most fashionable residents declaring that they live in hovels while some of the paupers insist on describing their huts as palaces with marble walls.

INSPECTOR. And how long have these scandals been going on?

MAYOR. Since the ghost first appeared.

INSPECTOR. I'll thank you not to use that stupid phrase, Mr. Mayor. Ghosts don't exist. Therefore they don't appear. *(Crosses Left.)*

MAYOR. Well, then, spirits.

INSPECTOR. Science tells us plainly that there are no spirits.

DOCTOR. That isn't what science tells us, Inspector. Science tells us, on the contrary, that many things have spirits. There are spirits of ammonia, spirits of nitre, spirits of camphor—

INSPECTOR. But not spirits of man.

DOCTOR. That's not so clear.

(The voices of the MANGEBOIS SISTERS *are heard offstage.* DOCTOR *goes up Left;* SUPERVISOR *rises;* MAYOR *crosses to Left Center.)*

ARMANDE. *(Still offstage)* May we come in, Mr. Mayor?

MAYOR. Come in, please. And shut the door behind

you. I mean—come in. Come in. *(The* SISTERS *enter up Right. They are spinsters. The elder,* LEONIDE MANGEBOIS, *is deaf, and wears a hearing aid by means of which the younger,* ARMANDE, *keeps her in touch with the conversation.* LEONIDE *crosses down to Right of stump;* ARMANDE *is Left of it.)* These ladies, Inspector, have an important disclosure to make. *(He bows)* The daughters of the late Justice Mangebois. It was he, you may recall, who issued the famous order for the separation of the Siamese twins of Poiters, when they both fell in love with the Italian tenor. (MAYOR *sits on stump.)*

INSPECTOR. Yes, I remember very well: a true judgment of Solomon.—Well, ladies?

ARMANDE. Inspector, it is my duty first of all to inform you that my sister Leonide is a little hard of hearing.

LEONIDE. What did you say?

ARMANDE. You are a little hard of hearing.

LEONIDE. Thank you. I don't need to be reminded.

ARMANDE. But, Leonide, since you insist on my repeating everything—

LEONIDE. You don't have to repeat what I already know.

ARMANDE. But the Inspector—

INSPECTOR. Ladies, if you have a statement to make before this committee—

LEONIDE. You snore. Do I tell?

ARMANDE. I do not snore.

LEONIDE. Then you must have stopped snoring the moment I stopped hearing.

INSPECTOR. Mademoiselle, kindly ask your sister to be quiet.

ARMANDE. Oh, I couldn't. She's my elder by five years.

LEONIDE. What's that?

ARMANDE. Nothing of interest.

LEONIDE. Then come to the point. And stop discussing my age.

ARMANDE. The Inspector calls for silence, Leonide.

LEONIDE. If he knew what silence was, he wouldn't want it. Well—go on. I'm listening.

INSPECTOR. *(Sits on log)* I am told, ladies, that you are informed of everything that goes on in the community.

ARMANDE. We are co-chairmen of the Ladies Aid.

INSPECTOR. Ah. And what, may I ask, is the current topic of discussion at the Ladies Aid?

ARMANDE. Why, naturally,—the ghost.

INSPECTOR. Do you believe this ghost exists?

ARMANDE. I do.

INSPECTOR. Have you ever seen it?

ARMANDE. I have seen people who have seen it.

INSPECTOR. What sort of people?

ARMANDE. One of them is a Commander of the Great Dragon of Annam.

INSPECTOR. If he believes in that, he'd believe in anything.—What are the names of these people?

ARMANDE. Madame Duval, the baker. And Commandant Lescallard, retired. It's the Commandant who is the Commander.

INSPECTOR. I could have guessed it. And according to the Commander, what does this ghost look like? A bedsheet, on a broom, I suppose, with a pumpkin on top, and a candle inside?

ARMANDE. The ghost is a pale young man dressed in black. He wears no hat. He is seen just at nightfall. And always here, near the edge of the lake.

INSPECTOR. Have there been any other phantoms prowling about the neighborhood?

ARMANDE. Never. Never before the crime.

INSPECTOR. Aha! Now we come to the crime!

MAYOR. *(Rises, crosses down)* Please don't say anything against the crime, Inspector. (LEONIDE *sits on stump.* ARMANDE *crosses to Right of stump.)* It was a superb example of a crime of passion, the only one ever to take place in this jurisdiction. I shall always

look back upon it with emotion and pride. It was the
crowning-point of my career.

INSPECTOR. It was a routine shooting, of which the
only interesting aspect was the extraordinary stupidity
of the police.

SUPERVISOR. It was a beautiful crime. A crime of
taste and distinction.

INSPECTOR. Did anyone here personally know the
assassin? Did you?

MAYOR. No. All we know about him is that he ar-
rived from Paris on the night train, and came directly
to the chateau where his wife and his friend were
spending the week-end together.

(ARMANDE *to above stump.*)

INSPECTOR. Did anyone see his face?

MAYOR. No. But the station master positively iden-
tified his hat.

INSPECTOR. So that, after shooting his wife and his
friend, he simply vanished? Except for his hat?

SUPERVISOR. He didn't vanish at all. He's right here.
In the lake.

INSPECTOR. What makes you so certain that he
drowned himself?

MAYOR. What possible doubt can there be? His hat
was found at the water's edge. As he stepped into the
lake, he took off his hat—

INSPECTOR. —And said "how do you do" to the
hereafter. Very touching. But the body was not found.

DOCTOR. The lake is deep.

INSPECTOR. So is the young man.

MAYOR. No, no, no, Inspector. The young man is
above suspicion. All the roads were watched. The
countryside was combed for weeks. The coroner's inquest established the suicide beyond a reasonable
doubt.

INSPECTOR. *(To* ARMANDE*)* Is that what you think?

ARMANDE. *(Crossing in.* LEONIDE *rises and follows.)*

It is our opinion that the drowned man has come back in the form of a ghost.

INSPECTOR. He might have come back without being a ghost. A murderer returns to the scene of the crime like a boomerang to the hand of the thrower.

LEONIDE. What's he saying?

ARMANDE. That a boomerang returns to the hand of the thrower.

LEONIDE. Amazing!

INSPECTOR. So you believe that the scandalous behavior reported in this community is all due to this ghost?

ARMANDE. Oh no, Inspector. Not at all. We know who's at the bottom of that.

INSPECTOR. You do?

ARMANDE. Of course. That's an entirely different line of activity. But we do think that these lines are converging. It won't be long before they meet. And when they do—! That's why we thought you should take action at once. Inspector— I don't know how much of the scandal has been reported to you—

INSPECTOR. I've heard all about it.

ARMANDE. You are aware of everything?

INSPECTOR. *(Impatiently)* I am aware, Madam, that at the moment, this district is completely arse over tip.

LEONIDE. What does the Inspector say?

ARMANDE. Nothing in particular.

LEONIDE. Armande, I insist that you repeat the end of each important sentence, as always.

ARMANDE. Arse over tip.

LEONIDE. Ah—! You are discussing Madame Lambert.

ARMANDE. We are not discussing Madame Lambert.

LEONIDE. No? Then who else can it be?

INSPECTOR. Ladies! I was not aware that Madame Lambert was in any way embraced in this discussion.

ARMANDE. You may not be aware of it, but Madame Lambert is embraced in every way, and by everybody. Except her husband.

(DOCTOR *crosses around above stump.*)

SUPERVISOR. I consider that an utterly false and malicious piece of slander. Madame Lambert is not embraced by everybody!

INSPECTOR. Mr. Supervisor, don't you think our task is sufficiently difficult without your dragging in Madame Lambert?

SUPERVISOR. I have no intention of dragging her in. But so long as she has been wantonly attacked, it is my obvious duty to defend her. Madame Lambert is one of the glories of France!

ARMANDE. He's mad.

MAYOR. Mr. Supervisor, please. This is neither the time nor the place— (*To Left, above log.*)

SUPERVISOR. Whoever is so fortunate as to catch a glimpse of Madame Lambert bending over the counter of her shop as she buckles a watch on a young man's wrist or opens a locket with the tip of a rosy nail, will gladly concede that the chief glory of France is neither its cathedrals nor its chateaux, but this young woman who with her delicate figure and her charming smile, reminds us from day to day that life is worth living.

(MAYOR *to Left below log.*)

LEONIDE. What is the Supervisor talking about?

ARMANDE. Absolutely nothing.

SUPERVISOR. I am saying, Madam, that wherever she is—and in our country I am glad to say she is everywhere—Madame Lambert is a living proof of the imperishable beauty of France. I gladly pay her this homage, and I will defend her honor to the last drop of my blood!

(DOCTOR *works up Left.*)

INSPECTOR. (*Rising*) Bravo. The inquest is adjourned.

ARMANDE. And I suppose you would say as much for Miss Isabel!

SUPERVISOR. *(Crossing Right)* Miss Isabel is the soul of purity. Whoever dares breathe a word against Miss Isabel will have to reckon with me.

MAYOR. And with me.

DOCTOR. *(Coming down)* And with me.

ARMANDE. Oh, you men! You're as blind as bats! *(Crosses to* MAYOR, LEONIDE *follows.)* Did it ever occur to you, Mr. Mayor, to ask your little niece what this soul of purity is teaching her?

(DOCTOR *goes up.)*

MAYOR. No. What is she teaching her?

ARMANDE. It's not for me to say. But it would be easy enough for you to find out. The Inspector is here. He has the right to examine her class, if he so desires.

INSPECTOR. *(Breaking Right)* It would doubtless be refreshing. But I have other problems, Madame.

ARMANDE. Then you don't wish to know who is disturbing the community?

DOCTOR. Do you think we shall find out by examining a class of little girls?

ARMANDE. Leonide, the time has come. Tell these gentlemen what you know.

LEONIDE. What I know? Why naturally I know everything. I have her diary.

INSPECTOR. Her diary? Where did you get it?

ARMANDE. Her diary? Where did you get it?

LEONIDE. You know perfectly well where I got it. You picked it up in the street, when she dropped it, and you handed it to me.

DOCTOR. You had the impudence to read it?

ARMANDE. You had the impudence to read it?

LEONIDE. I had to look it over, naturally, to see whose it was.

SUPERVISOR. And when you found out, why didn't you return it at once?

ARMANDE. And when you found out, why didn't you return it at once?

LEONIDE. *(Crossing to* MAYOR) Here, take it, Mr. Mayor. Open it anywhere. You will soon see what this angelic Isabel is doing right under your nose. Breaking up households! Turning dogs against their masters, children against their parents! Sending anonymous letters to people! Open it. Open it! Open to the 21st of March. You'll see if this creature is to be trusted with a class of little girls. 21st of March! What is he saying?

ARMANDE. *(To Center)* It's you that's talking.

INSPECTOR. Read the 21st of March.

MAYOR. *(To Center. Reading)* "March 21st. March 21st! Organized a little spring festival today for my children. Compared the beauty of nature with the beauty of the human form. As a practical class exercise, held an election for the most beautiful man in town. They unanimously elected the Supervisor of Weights and Measures. Not bad, children, not bad."

ARMANDE. You see what I mean?

INSPECTOR. Mr. Supervisor— *(He looks him up and down critically)* Be so good as to ask this young woman to report here at once with her class.—Ah, I could have sworn there was a woman at the bottom of this! Whoever set these termites loose in the social structure was no friend to man! Good God, there's not a sound timber left in it!

SUPERVISOR. *(Turning back)* Inspector—

INSPECTOR. You heard my order?

SUPERVISOR. *(A step Right)* Yes sir. But before I go, I should like to call your attention to certain fundamental differences between ants and women.

INSPECTOR. Don't trouble. They're exactly the same to me.

LEONIDE. What's he say?

ARMANDE. An ant is the same to him as a woman.

LEONIDE. Is he married?

INSPECTOR. No, Madam. I am not. Nevertheless, I

find them indistinguishable. Same senseless hustle and bustle. Same endless gossip whenever they meet. Same cruelty to outsiders. And their pinched-in figures. And the bundles they're always carrying. Absolutely the same species of insect.

SUPERVISOR. Inspector—if you would give yourself the trouble one day to turn an ant over on its back, and, very delicately, with the tip of your finger—

INSPECTOR. Are you or are you not going to find that young woman?

(SUPERVISOR *bows and goes off down Right.*)

MAYOR. I don't see what Isabel has to do with this. We're here to investigate a ghost, not a girl.

ARMANDE. In this case, Mr. Mayor, it's the same thing.

DOCTOR. Are you suggesting that Isabel is a witch?

ARMANDE. Read the 14th of May.

INSPECTOR. The 14th of May? That was yesterday.

ARMANDE. For a long time my sister and I have been wondering why Isabel invariably chooses this spot for her evening walk. The 14th of May gives us the answer.

INSPECTOR. Be so kind as to read it.

MAYOR. *(Reads)* "May 14th. Today I feel sure that the ghost knows what I am doing, and that he wants to help me. I know he is dying to speak to me. But, poor thing, he's terribly shy. The moment I come near him, he vanishes in embarrassment. All the same, he's certain to take the final step within a day or two. And when he does, what wonderful things he will have to tell me! And what wonderful things we shall do! Together we shall make the town perfect—and after the town, the district—and after that—who knows?— perhaps the world! I have a feeling it will be to-morrow!"

INSPECTOR. And tomorrow is today.

(MAYOR *crosses Left above log.*)

LEONIDE. What does the Inspector say?

ARMANDE. That tomorrow is today.

LEONIDE. He has a right to his opinion.

SUPERVISOR. *(Enters with blueboard, down Right to below stump)* Miss Isabel is coming at once.

ARMANDE. *(Crossing to Left of* LEONIDE*)* In that case, we'd better go. Come, Leonide.

INSPECTOR. *(To Left Center)* Ladies, I thank you for your invaluable assistance. Very soon now, I trust, we shall be in a position to contemplate the naked truth.

ARMANDE. Failing that, gentlemen, you always have Madame Lambert.

LEONIDE. What?

ARMANDE. He always has Madame Lambert.

LEONIDE. Oh!

ARMANDE. Good day, Supervisor.

(As SISTERS *leave down Left,* ISABEL *enters Right with her class.* INSPECTOR *to Left Center;* SUPERVISOR *to above log.* MARIE-LOUISE, DAISY, IRENE *down Right below* ISABEL; OTHERS *above* ISABEL.*)*

ISABEL. *(At Right)* You wish to see me, Inspector?

SUPERVISOR. If the ants looked like that—!

INSPECTOR. I have received very strange reports, Miss, concerning your methods of instruction.

ISABEL. I don't understand. What sort of reports?

INSPECTOR. *(Sits on log)* I shall have to examine your class. Please ask them to come in. (GIRLS *giggle.*) Why are they giggling?

ISABEL. They can't come in. You'll have to come out.

INSPECTOR. These open air classes are ridiculous! (GIRLS *start whispering.*) Silence! If I catch one of you talking she will have to stand with her head in a corner. A tree, that is. *(Laughter.)* Your pupils evidently have not the slightest idea of discipline.

MAYOR. *(Sitting on log)* They're really very cute, Inspector.

INSPECTOR. A well-disciplined class is never "cute." A well-disciplined class has the sage and serious look of an empty checkerboard.

DOCTOR. You'll never get these children to look like that.

INSPECTOR. And why not, if you please?

DOCTOR. They're much too gay.

INSPECTOR. I know of nothing in the school regulations that requires children to be gay. But there is a good deal about their being orderly. If they are gay, it is because their teacher doesn't punish them properly.

ISABEL. Why in the world should I punish them?

INSPECTOR. How do you expect to gain their respect if you don't punish them? (LITTLE GIRLS *titter again.*) Now what is it?

MAYOR. There is a caterpillar crawling on your collar.

INSPECTOR. *(Grimly)* There is!

ISABEL. *(To Left Center)* Oh, please don't kill it. It's a *collata azurea.* And it isn't doing anything wrong. Only what nature intended.

INSPECTOR. I have yet to read in any work on biology that nature intended the *collata azurea* to crawl on an Inspector's collar. *(He kills it.* GIRLS *begin to weep.)* What are you crying about?

LUCY. You killed the *collata azurea!*

INSPECTOR. And suppose a thrush had gobbled it up? You'd think that was wonderful, I suppose.

LUCY. It's natural for the thrush to eat it. Are you going to eat it?

INSPECTOR. No! Enough of this foolishness. The examination will begin. Who is at the head of the class?

(GIRLS *look at each other in wonder.*)

ISABEL. Nobody, Inspector.
INSPECTOR. What?

ISABEL. They're all at the head of the class.

INSPECTOR. Hm. You mean they're all at the foot.—
You there—what is your best subject?

(ISABEL *leads* GILBERTE *to Center and steps back.*).

GILBERTE. Botany, sir.

INSPECTOR. Explain the difference between a mono-
cotyledon and dicotyledon.

GILBERTE. I said, botany, sir.

INSPECTOR. Astounding ignorance! You don't even
think that's botany, eh? Does she know what a tree is?

GILBERTE. She does, sir.

ISABEL. *(Crossing to* GILBERTE) If you know the
answer, Gilberte, tell the Inspector. He's listening.
(Steps back.)

GILBERTE. A tree is a tall person who is rooted to
the ground. He spreads out his arms and holds his
stomach in his hands. In tree language, a murderer is
called a woodcutter, a corpse is called lumber, and
woodpeckers are fleas.

INSPECTOR. There is no tree-language in the Indo-
European linguistic group. Zero. (GILBERTE *claps her
hands joyfully and goes back to her place.)* What is
she so happy about?

ISABEL. In our class, zero is the highest mark. It's
closest to infinity.

INSPECTOR. Very interesting system. Perhaps you'd
better continue. They don't seem to understand me.

ISABEL. *(Leads* DAISY *to Center)* Explain the flower,
Daisy.

DAISY. *(Facing ¾ front)* The flower is one of the
most beautiful aspects of nature—

INSPECTOR. Good. *(To the* MAYOR) That's a little
more like it.

DAISY. It is a practical demonstration of the beauty
of the sexual process.

INSPECTOR. What did she say?

DAISY. The flower is the poetry of reproduction. It

is an example of the eternal seductiveness of nature.

INSPECTOR. One moment!

DAISY. But like all coquettes, the flower has its practical side. Its beauty is meant to attract the bee, which deposits upon its pistil the pollen of other flowers. In this manner, plants are married. In a very different way from birds—

INSPECTOR. Enough!

DAISY. Or fish—

INSPECTOR. Stop, I say!

DAISY. And especially the higher mammals, which are provided with—

INSPECTOR. *(Rises. Shouts)* Silence! Is there no end to these indecencies? (MAYOR *rises.)* —Good heavens!

(DAISY *curtseys and goes back to her place.)*

MAYOR. Better try geography.

INSPECTOR. Never mind. I've heard enough.

MAYOR. You—my little Viola— (VIOLA *to Center.)* —what causes earthquakes?

VIOLA. *(Curtseys and returns to place)* It's the Harmonizer, Mr. Mayor.

INSPECTOR. The what?

VIOLA. The Harmonizer.

INSPECTOR. What nonsense have you been teaching them?

ISABEL. I can't believe that it is good for children to think of nature as cruel and destructive. Therefore I have explained that, while these natural castastrophes are disagreeable in themselves, they are necessary for the good of the whole. The power that destroys things in the interests of the ultimate harmony, we call the Harmonizer.

INSPECTOR. I see. So it is the Harmonizer who keeps banging the shutters in the middle of the night. It is the Harmonizer who splashes gravy on your shirt front at an official dinner.

VIOLA. Oh no! No. That's Arthur! That's Arthur!

INSPECTOR. What? That's Arthur? Aha! So it's Arthur that makes caterpillars crawl on the Inspector's collar?

THE GIRLS. Arthur! Arthur!

INSPECTOR. Hm-hm. And then Arthur makes the Inspector kill the caterpillar?

THE GIRLS. Oh, no, oh no—! The Harmonizer!

INSPECTOR. I give up. *(Crossing to* MAYOR) Mr. Mayor, I must confess that in thirty years of departmental administration, I have never seen anything like this.

MAYOR. Perhaps if we tried them in history?

INSPECTOR. Is it possible that you don't yet see where this system of education tends? Its aim is nothing less than the release of these young minds from the net of truth in which our magnificent twentieth century has finally caught the universe. No matter what you ask them—history, geography, arithmetic—the result will be precisely the same. I'll show you. *(Crossing in Left Center)* You, there—what is France bounded by?

IRENE. *(Crosses in)* The love of its neighbors. *(Returns to place.)*

INSPECTOR. You see? You—what is a right angle?

LUCY. *(Crosses in)* There is no such thing as a right angle. A right angle is what one imagines when one is weary of curves. *(Returns to place.)*

INSPECTOR. You see? You—how much is two and two?

DAISY. *(Crosses in)* Four.

INSPECTOR. *(To* MAYOR) You see?—Ah! I beg pardon! These children are enough to make me lose my wits! Besides, how does it happen that for them also two and two make four? By what idiotic train of thought does this child arrive at the truth? I am certain that her four is no real four, but a five in disguise. Tell the truth, now—two and two are five. Right?

DAISY. No, sir. Four. *(Returns to place.)*

INSPECTOR. And stubborn too!— *(To* DENISE) You, there. Sing the *Marseillaise!*

MAYOR. I don't think it's included in their syllabus.

INSPECTOR. I said, sing the *Marseillaise!* Of course, she doesn't know it.

ISABEL. *(Leading* DENISE *to Center)* Oh, she does, Inspector.

DENISE. I do. I do. *(She sings)*
Every little girl enjoys
The thought that there are little boys—
And if they're very good and brush their curls,
The boys will love the little girls.
(Returns to place.)

INSPECTOR. So that's the *Marseillaise!* I might have known. *(Crosses Right. Looks)* And this red mark you all have on your necks—what is that? A vaccination? *(Crosses up.)*

LUCY. No sir. It's the mark for the spirits.

INSPECTOR. What?

LUCY. It's the mark by which the spirits recognize their friends. Isabel puts it on us every morning—with her lipstick.

INSPECTOR. Rub it off.

THE GIRLS. Oh no! Oh no!

VIOLA. We'd be afraid.

THE GIRLS. We'd be afraid.

INSPECTOR. Rub it off at once or I'll—

THE GIRLS. No, no— The Spirit wouldn't like it!

INSPECTOR. *(To Center)* Now listen to me, all of you. (GIRLS *step in.* DOCTOR *crosses to above stump.)* After we die, there are no spirits. There are only bones and worms. You will all commit that to memory at once. Repeat after me. After we die—

THE GIRLS. After we die—

INSPECTOR. There are no spirits—

THE GIRLS. There are so spirits—

INSPECTOR. What did you say?

DOCTOR. Why disillusion the children, Inspector? They'd much rather be spirits than bones and worms. Wouldn't you?

INSPECTOR. *(Turns Left)* Completely asinine ques-

tion. The facts are the facts. Death is nothing but
bones and worms. And as for life— *(Turns Right)*
Listen to me, you! Life is nothing but a tiresome jour-
ney. (DOCTOR *goes up Right.)* For a man, it consists
of false starts, snail-like advances, nasty setbacks, and
lost collar buttons. For a woman, it consists of chatter
and clatter, shopping and mopping. There—now you
have me talking in poetry.

SUPERVISOR. It's beautiful. Don't stop.

INSPECTOR. Young lady, (ISABEL *steps in.)* as I understand it, on your own responsibility, and without
the slightest regard for the official syllabus, you have
undertaken to teach your pupils the way to happiness—

ISABEL. I teach them what God has in store for them.

INSPECTOR. Nonsense. It says nowhere in the Bible
that when God created the world, He created happiness. Day and night, yes. But not Happiness. What
He created was certain compensations for the habitual
misery of humanity—such as fishing, bridge, and
love. You have deliberately misled these children as to
the nature of life. And that is conduct unbecoming a
teacher.

ISABEL. I can only teach what I believe.

INSPECTOR. Very nice. Very heroic. You are relieved
of your post, effective immediately.

(ISABEL *goes up and* GIRLS *group around her, "Oh
no" etc.* SUPERVISOR *to below log.)*

MAYOR. *(Crosses to* INSPECTOR) But, Inspector, I
have no other available substitute. The regular teacher
is having a baby.

INSPECTOR. That's no concern of mine.

MAYOR. I asked Paris for a substitute over six weeks
ago. But instead of a teacher they sent me an assistant to the Assistant Supervisor of Weights and Measures. Can you understand that?

INSPECTOR. Not entirely. But I can remedy it. *(Looks
around)* Mr. Supervisor. (SUPERVISOR *crosses in.)* I

am transferring you to temporary duty in the Education department. Until Paris sees fit to send a proper substitute, you will have charge of this class.

SUPERVISOR. But I haven't the slightest qualifications for teaching a class of little girls. What in the world could I teach them?

INSPECTOR. Weights and measures. (GIRLS *begin to move down Right.)* And where are you going, may I ask? Who dismissed you? The Harmonizer?

ISABEL. *(Coming down Right)* You may go now, children.

INSPECTOR. Two by two and mouth shut. *(The* GIRLS *form in twos.)* Take charge of your class, Supervisor. (SUPERVISOR *crosses Right below* GIRLS.) What's that you're carrying there?

GILBERTE. The blueboard, sir.

INSPECTOR. The blueboard can stay here. With the pink chalk and the turquoise ink and the sea-green pencil. From now on, you're going to have a blackboard, and black ink—yes, and black pinafores. There's no color like black for the education of the young. Two by two. And no talking. (GIRLS *exit down Right in twos, followed by* SUPERVISOR.) Ah—now they're beginning to look like a class. One month's discipline, and you won't be able to tell them one from the other. As for you, Miss, I am going to write your parents this very day. Come, gentlemen. We shall continue our investigation in the Mayor's office. *(Crosses Left, above log)* Where's my hat? (GIRLS *peek out Right entrance.)* Now who the devil put a hedgehog in my hat?

VIOLA. Arthur—

THE GIRLS. Arthur! Arthur!

INSPECTOR. *(Crossing Right)* Arthur!

(ALL *exit, save* ISABEL *and the* DOCTOR.)

ISABEL. You have something to tell me, Doctor?

DOCTOR. No, Isabel.

ISABEL. Oh. Was there something you wanted to ask?

DOCTOR. No. I am only waiting a moment—for the transition.

ISABEL. Transition?

DOCTOR. *(At Center)* At my age, Isabel, one comes to a pretty clear realization of the part one is destined to play in this world. Some are cast as villains, some can be heroes. My role is a modest one. I am used to making transitions. I am a sort of usher.

ISABEL. *(Sits on stump)* You are?

DOCTOR. *(Steps in)* You see, my dear, quite often in passing from a moment on one level to a moment on another level, nature has to make use of a bridge. Between, for example, a foolish moment and a moment of solemnity—obviously, by itself the one could never become the other. To fuse the precise with the vague, the ridiculous with the sublime—that is my function. Whenever it happens that the past and the future are not on speaking terms, I appear. I take the hand of the past, I give it to the future, and the one is joined to the other.

ISABEL. But that is a beautiful role!

DOCTOR. It's useful, perhaps, but not glamorous. However, there is no use my trying to get away from it; everyone knows what I am meant to do in this world. Have you noticed? Whenever someone is needed to interrupt a tennis match with news of an accident, or to break into a funeral with word of a spectacular stroke of fortune, it's always I. Well—

ISABEL. Are you going to make a transition now?

DOCTOR. *(Crossing to log)* Over this stupid situation into which the Inspector has thrust us, nature is striving to bring a moment of quiet and sweetness. Without me, it would perhaps not be possible.

ISABEL. I see.

DOCTOR. *(Crossing to ISABEL)* Then also, there is the transition to manage between the Isabel we know and another Isabel—an ethereal, transparent, and ineffably lovely Isabel, of whom as yet we can only surmise the quality—

ISABEL. What are you going to do?

DOCTOR. Watch closely.

ISABEL. It will be difficult?

DOCTOR. *(A step Left)* It will be incredibly easy. With you, Isabel, in order to transform the most vulgar and prosaic moment into a time of mystery and romance, all I need is a mere nothing—a gesture: this gesture. A silence—this silence. You see? It's almost done. And now my assistants—listen. (ISABEL *rises.)* The owl. The frogs. The crickets. The overture begins. All we need now is for you to pronounce the name of the moment—

ISABEL. *(Crossing to Left entrance)* Aloud?

DOCTOR. *(To above log)* Please.

ISABEL. The twilight.

DOCTOR. Yes. And when it is twilight, what sound is it that echoes always from a little French town?

ISABEL. *(To Left end of log)* The trumpets of the garrison.

(A fanfare of TRUMPETS is heard in the distance.)

DOCTOR. And when the trumpets are quiet, what is it that rises among the weeds and the willows, moving through the shadows of cypress and pine, itself hardly more than a shadow?

ISABEL. *(Smiling)* The ghost.

DOCTOR. *(Vanishing down Left)* There. You see? It's done. *(Exits.)*

(ISABEL *sits down, takes out her pocket glass and adjusts her make-up. THE GHOST appears behind her. She watches him for a moment in her mirror—a young man, very pale, hatless. He too, gazes at her, and for a long moment, their eyes meet. As she lowers her mirror, it flashes the last rays of the setting sun at the dark figure, which seems to shudder as the light touches it.)*

ISABEL. Forgive me. Did I hurt you?

GHOST. I am a little sensitive to light. (ISABEL *turns.*)
But now it is only moonlight.

ISABEL. You do hear the words of the living?

GHOST. I hear your words.

ISABEL. I wanted so much to talk with you.

GHOST. About what?

ISABEL. About life. About your friends. The spirits.
You must know a great deal about spirits?

GHOST. I am learning.

ISABEL. Will you teach me?

GHOST. What is your name?

ISABEL. What difference does it make? You seem
so serious. Do you have to be? I'm sure they smile
sometimes—

GHOST. Who?

ISABEL. The dead.

GHOST. Why would they smile?

ISABEL. But surely—when something funny happens
in the other world—

GHOST. Something funny in the other world?

ISABEL. Or something touching, or surprising.
Aren't there comic spirits, aren't there clumsy spirits?
Don't you joke sometimes? Or slip? Or stumble?

GHOST. What could make a spirit slip, or stumble?

ISABEL. Well, whatever in the other world corre-
sponds to a banana peel or a curbstone—the thought
of a banana peel, the memory of a curbstone.

GHOST. The dead are extremely agile. They never
stumble. They never smile.

ISABEL. But, here is what puzzles me most of all.
How can the dead believe in death? With us, of course,
it's different. Since it's good to think that fatness and
falsehood will have an end one day, we are forced to
concede that kindness and beauty, which are so much
more fragile, will also die. But the spirits—refined
and free of flesh—how can they be so silly as to believe in death?

GHOST. You expect the dead to believe in life?

ISABEL. At least in the life of the spirit. May I be

quite frank? It often seems to me that the dead are a little relaxed. They let themselves drift. I don't mean you, of course—you're different, you're trying. But don't you agree that if the dead had a little more initiative, a little more aggressiveness, it would be so much better for us all? If only they would give us— those who are trying, I mean—their attention, their support, what marvellous lives we could lead—in both our worlds! Do you think it would be hard to get them to help us? All we need really is some energetic soul to stir them up a bit.

GHOST. Perhaps they're waiting for you.

ISABEL. *(Rises)* I am coming as fast as I can. Only I'm not at all sure that I will be particularly useful once I'm dead. I'm afraid that what would appeal to me most about death would be the laziness of death, the lovely thick torpor of death in which the dead seem to wallow. No. What I am able to do, I must do now while I'm alive.

GHOST. And just what is it you wish to do?

ISABEL. Dear ghost, I have always dreamed of one day doing something really wonderful. For humanity. Something that would save the world from itself, and make life as sensible and happy as a fairy tale.

GHOST. Really?

ISABEL. It isn't easy to help the living, believe me. I know. I've tried. They're so heavy, so stupid, so steeped in the flesh that they're afraid to move. But the dead are so light—so wise—and so gentle! If only I could get them to help me, what a wonderful, wonderful world we could make!

GHOST. You want the dead to come back to the world?

ISABEL. I want so much to make them come back. I want to see them take the world by storm, sweep it clean of the cobwebs in which it is entangled, and make a bright new world in terms of the eternal life which is ours. We are afraid to live because we are afraid to die. But the dead have died; they know the magnitude and meaning of life. How easily they could teach us to live not like clods, but like spirits!—And really, what could be simpler? There is only the wall of silence between us. And there are loopholes in that wall.

GHOST. Where?   *(WARN Curtain.)*

ISABEL. Don't you know? You have come through it.

GHOST. True. I have come through it.

ISABEL. Oh, if only there could be found a young spirit, a spirit with energy and imagination! How easy it would be for us, he and I together, to rouse the others to a sense of adventure!

GHOST. The dead are not adventurous.

ISABEL. They could be.

GHOST. The dead are dead.

ISABEL. *(Crossing up)* What strange ideas people have about themselves! The white race thinks it's white. The yellow race thinks it's yellow. The race of the living believes that it's living; and the dead think they are dead. *(Down Left Center)* Do you think you're dead?

GHOST. Why—

ISABEL. You see? Death is nothing but a state of mind. And not a very reasonable one, really. Why can't we make the others see that? It's perfectly clear to me— Now tell me all about it. Tell me—what happens when you die? The very first thing?

GHOST. First tell me your name.

ISABEL. But, really, of what possible interest is my name? It's a name like any other.

GHOST. Where do you live?

ISABEL. In the town.—Now tell me.

GHOST. Well, the moment one dies—

ISABEL. Yes? *(He hesitates. She looks around)* We're quite alone. Go on. *(But the GHOST has vanished off Right.)* Where is he? Where are you? *(She looks about desperately)* Isabel! My name is Isabel! It's Isabel.

CURTAIN

ACT TWO

SCENE: *The same, from another point of view. The spring is more advanced, the trees are full, and the hedges have burst into flower.*
Some time before sunset.

AT RISE: *The* SUPERVISOR *on stump conducting a class in elementary astronomy. The* LITTLE GIRLS, *each bearing a flashlight, are being the stars of the sky.*

SUPERVISOR. The Triangle!

(GIRLS *form a sort of triangle, twinkling joyously.*)

THE GIRLS. *(As they form the figure, they sing)*
        Magellan stared with open mouth—
        He didn't know that in the south
        The starry Triangle is where
        We normally expect the Bear.
SUPERVISOR. The Compass!
THE GIRLS. *(Dance into compass)*
        There is a Compass in the sky
        But our advice is, never mind it,
        It's just as well to pass it by
        You need two compasses to find it.
SUPERVISOR. The Clock!

(GIRLS *begin to form the Clock, but the* DOCTOR *interrupts, entering from down Left.*)

DOCTOR. Good afternoon, children. Playing in the woods again?

SUPERVISOR. No. They're playing in the sky.

THE GIRLS. Good night, Doctor! Good night, Doctor!

DOCTOR. Why good night? It's still afternoon. *(Noticing* GILBERTE*)* —What is she doing?

GILBERTE. I'm being Alpha Centauri.

SUPERVISOR. Doctor, be careful; you are streaking across the southern sky like a comet. Sit down here. Lift your light a little, Gilberte. You are of the first magnitude, you know.

DOCTOR. What's going on here?

SUPERVISOR. Astronomy.

DOCTOR. Oh, I see. Well, it's going to be a magnificent night for stars, children. Tonight you will see them come out one by one, all of them, even the faintest.

SUPERVISOR. *(Crosses above stump)* I'm afraid they won't see any, not even the brightest. The Inspector requires all my students to be in bed by sundown.

DOCTOR. You mean these children never see the stars overhead?

SUPERVISOR. No. They have to look down to see them. In the interests of proper discipline, we study the southern sky exclusively. At this moment my class is plunged in sub-equatorial darkness.

DOCTOR. Do they really know the southern stars?

SUPERVISOR. They know only the southern stars.— Daisy, where is the Furnace?

DAISY. Just under the Doctor's foot.

(The DOCTOR *hastily removes his foot.)*

SUPERVISOR. The nice thing about the southern sky is that the ancients never saw it. It was discovered and baptized during the age of reason. The result is that instead of a sky peopled with monsters, the southerners have a sky full of laboratory equipment—the Clock, the Furnace, the Compass, the Microscope, even the Air Pump. It's a regular heaven for children.—Viola, jump from the Triangle to the Telescope.

VIOLA. By way of the Furnace?

SUPERVISOR. No. The Doctor is on the Furnace. Over the Table.

VIOLA. *(She hesitates)* It's quite a jump, you know. It's thirty million billion miles.

SUPERVISOR. Take two jumps. *(She jumps.)* That's it. Now, children, the Southern Cross.

THE GIRLS. *(They form the Cross, singing)*
Laperouse was quite excited
When first the Southern Cross he sighted—
There really isn't any use
For steeples now, said Laperouse.

SUPERVISOR. *(Sits on log)* The only trouble with this sort of astronomy is that one tends to think of the sky as a floor instead of a roof. For them, the stars are not beacons, but stepping stones.

DOCTOR. *(Sits on log)* Don't worry about that. To each little girl there comes a night when suddenly she turns a somersault, and forever after the stars are overhead.

SUPERVISOR. Oh, they're in love already. All of them.

DOCTOR. They are? With whom? With you?

SUPERVISOR. With the ghost, of course.

LUCY. And so is Isabel! And so is Isabel!

SUPERVISOR. Lucy, that's naughty. You shall be punished. From now on, you're a dead star. Put out your light. Well? Are you going out?

LUCY. It takes two million years for a star to die.

SUPERVISOR. *(Rising)* It only takes us two seconds. Out with you. Besides, it's time for recess. Vanish—!! *(Crosses Right.)*

(GIRLS *run off Right.*)

DOCTOR. *(Crossing to Center)* You find Isabel rather interesting, don't you?

SUPERVISOR. *(Crossing in)* Everyone finds Isabel interesting. Even the Inspector.

DOCTOR. Oh?

SUPERVISOR. There's no longer any use pretending.

The ghost is more and more in evidence all the time, and wherever he is, Isabel is with him. The Inspector is getting a daily report of all her activities.

DOCTOR. What if he is? There's no law against being friendly with ghosts.

SUPERVISOR. To be friendly with ghosts is to be ghostly. People are gossiping. Besides, you don't really think that this ghost of hers is a ghost?

DOCTOR. I think he soon will be.

SUPERVISOR. I don't follow.

DOCTOR. I have a distinct impression that before long we are going to witness the birth of a phantom. A real phantom.

SUPERVISOR. How? Why?

DOCTOR. I don't know. But everything we have seen in the past weeks points toward some monstrous birth. Depend on it, Supervisor, Nature is hatching a surprise for us. It was after some such series of events as these, that one day, before the eyes of the astonished animals, the first man took shape.

SUPERVISOR. There is certainly something queer going on.

DOCTOR. Yes, our town is possessed. It is in that strange condition when every dream comes true and every wish is granted. In an individual that would be called a state of ecstasy. That's it: Our town is in a state of ecstasy. *(To below stump.)*

SUPERVISOR. It's strange. This morning for no good reason, I dreamt of a chimpanzee. And as I opened the front door to take in the milk, what do you suppose was the first thing my eyes lit on? A chimpanzee. True, it was a tame chimpanzee on the end of a leash held by a gypsy. Nevertheless, there was my dream sitting on my doorstep.

DOCTOR. It's just as well you didn't dream of a crocodile. I tell you, my boy, we're in an uncanny state, all of us—we're in the vein, like a gambler who can't lose. Nature is pampering us. Why?

SUPERVISOR. *(Crossing to* DOCTOR*)* Doctor, while

this lasts, we mustn't let Isabel out of our sight for a moment. This is no joke.

DOCTOR. You're right. Nature never jokes. When mountains give birth, it is never mice that issue forth from their wombs, but thunder and lightning. Everything here is collaborating to produce a phantom—the light, the darkness, our fears, our imagination, the other world perhaps, and certainly the Inspector. *(Enter the* INSPECTOR *down Left.)* You see? The Inspector.

(The MAYOR *follows to Left of* INSPECTOR. DOCTOR *sits on stump.)*

INSPECTOR. Gentlemen, I called this meeting for a very definite purpose. I have here a letter sent by special courier from the government. Be so good as to read it, Mr. Mayor. It particularly concerns you.

MAYOR. *(Taking the letter which the* INSPECTOR *hands him, he glances over the contents)* You really think it concerns me?

INSPECTOR. Every bit as much as myself. Particularly, the last paragraph.

MAYOR. But the last paragraph particularly—

INSPECTOR. Read it. Read it aloud. I want you all to hear what the government says.

MAYOR. The government appears to be very warmly disposed toward you.

INSPECTOR. *(Crossing down Left)* I am happy to say it is.

MAYOR. It kisses you on your adorable mouth, asks you for a hundred francs, and signs itself, yours ever, Adele.

INSPECTOR. *(Crosses Center, grabs letter)* Oh, pardon. *(He fumbles in his breast pocket for other letter)* Here we are. Please! I must solicit your most earnest attention, Gentlemen. This is no laughing matter. *(Crosses Left.)*

MAYOR. *(Reading)* The Superior Council, after tak-

ing due note of the unusual phenomena that have been
reported in your district, congratulates itself upon the
fact that in our enlightened country, mass hysteria is
able to find a less hackneyed outlet than the customary
miracle. We felicitate our constituents upon their happy
choice of a middle course between primitive druidism
and contemporary radical thought, and on their triumph
over clerical superstition in this flowering of the native
folklore which is one of the glories of our national
heritage.

SUPERVISOR. What an elegant style! Who sits on the
Superior Council?

INSPECTOR. Why, naturally—the choicest spirits.

MAYOR. *(Continues reading)* Nevertheless, the char-
acter of the perturbations brought about by the alleged
phantom in the communal life of your district is judged
to be not sufficiently in accord with the ideals of the
Socialist party to warrant the tacit collaboration of
the government. Consequently the Council requests you
to take all necessary steps for the prompt liquidation
of this apparition, and for this purpose places at your
disposal all available military and civil powers with
full authority in the premises. For the Superior Council.
Duval, Secretary.

INSPECTOR. *(Sitting on log)* So. And now, gentlemen, we can proceed to wind up the case.

MAYOR. I don't know what there remains to wind,
Inspector. Since you took charge two weeks ago, we
have hardly left a stone unturned, and yet we have not
discovered a single subversive element in the entire
community.

INSPECTOR. What was yesterday's catch?

MAYOR. Nothing worth mentioning. A poodle dog
who was apparently trying to look like the Prime Minister. After he was lassoed and put in the pound, his
face relaxed into the expression of kindliness and
humanity that is normal with dogs. That is absolutely
all.

INSPECTOR. So. And what did you dream last night, my dear Mayor?

MAYOR. What I dreamt?

INSPECTOR. If the atmosphere of this jurisdiction is as pure as you say, the inhabitants should now be enjoying the most normal dreams in France. Do you happen to remember yours?

MAYOR. Why yes. I spent the night chasing two enormous ducks which, after many transformations, at last became my feet. It was absolutely maddening. It's no joke to chase your own feet all night, especially when they cackle. Toward morning I became a centipede. I awoke completely bewildered. *(Crosses up.)*

INSPECTOR. Hm. And you, Mr. Supervisor?

SUPERVISOR. *(Steps in Right Center)* It's a little embarrassing. If you don't mind—

INSPECTOR. Sorry. I must insist.

SUPERVISOR. Well—I dreamt I was madly in love with a woman who eluded my advances by springing back and forth over an open grave. She wore only a short cloak, with her right breast bare—and this woman was you.

INSPECTOR. Well! And now, Mr. Mayor, are you going to tell me that a dream like that, however flattering for me, can be for a moment considered a normal French dream? *(Rising)* Is this, multiplied by forty-two million, a product worthy of the nightly endeavors of the most rational and practical nation in the world?

SUPERVISOR. I doubt if sixty-four million sleeping Germans could do any better. *(Crosses up.)*

INSPECTOR. *(Crossing Right Center)* Gentlemen, you know as well as I that matters here are going from bad to worse!

DOCTOR. *(Rises; crossing Left)* Don't tell us, Inspector, that you are beginning to notice some supernatural influence?

INSPECTOR. Supernatural fiddle-faddle! Why not say plainly a conspiracy against constituted authority? And what is the object of it? (SUPERVISOR *and* DOCTOR *sit on log.)* Simply to bring the workings of our enlightened democracy into contempt and ridicule. And who are the members of this conspiracy? A young girl and a ghost? Nonsense. The whole town is involved, and you know it. (MAYOR *sits Left on log.)* Tell me, Doctor, how does it happen that every night at midnight, an unseen hand adds a thirteenth stroke to the hour? Eh? How is that the very moment a high government official sits on a public bench that bench miraculously becomes sticky with green paint? Hm? And why is it that at the café, the sugar in other people's coffee dissolves, but the sugar in my coffee never dissolves? What?—I give you fair warning, you and all of you, this radical nonsense has gone too far! This very evening we are going to have a showdown—you and Isabel and this ghost and I.

MAYOR. Isabel has nothing to do with this, Inspector.

INSPECTOR. Mr. Mayor, with the exception of yourself, apparently, everyone in town is aware that for the past two weeks Isabel has been keeping a nocturnal rendezvous with this ghost. Now, what is the object of these interviews?

MAYOR. I can't imagine.

INSPECTOR. It's quite clear to me that there is a concerted movement on foot here to undermine the basis of established government, which is founded, necessarily, on a sound acceptance of the fact that in this world we can never get what we want. There is entirely too much happiness in this community for the good of the nation. Everywhere you look, people are smiling and neglecting their work. The surrounding districts are beginning to ask questions. The movement is small, but these things spread like wildfire. Another week of this, and I should no longer be answerable for the consequences.

MAYOR. I fail to see the slightest connection with Isabel.

INSPECTOR. You may have noticed that every evening at six, Isabel drifts out of town with that air of false innocence that invariably characterizes those who harbor fugitives from justice. As her hands are always empty, I make no doubt that the food which she brings our invisible friend is none other than her youth, her tenderness and her vitality—a complete blue-plate for a ghost, and perhaps with dessert and coffee.

SUPERVISOR. *(Starts to rise)* I beg your pardon!

MAYOR. *(Rises; crossing to Center)* Just a moment. Just a moment. Inspector, you made a point of asking me to invite Isabel to lunch with us today. Tell me this—have you ever seen a more normal, healthy appetite?

INSPECTOR. Show me another girl with a figure like that who can put away a meal that big! It's perfectly obvious that this girl is eating for two. (MAYOR *breaks to Left.)* The only question is—who is the other?

DOCTOR. After all, Inspector, a young girl's metabolism—

INSPECTOR. Hm!—Mark my words—in some inexplicable manner this girl is passing on her excess calories to someone who does not eat! And just who this parasite is, I shall soon find out. Their meeting place is not far off. I know the place well. It's precisely here.

MAYOR. What are you planning? An ambush?

INSPECTOR. An ambush.

SUPERVISOR. Inspector, Isabel likes to chat with me from time to time. Before we do anything, let me speak with her. Let me point out the dangers of her position. Let me warn her that—

INSPECTOR. Tonight, I intend once and for all to put an end to the influence of Isabel in this community.

DOCTOR. And may I ask what means you intend to employ?

INSPECTOR. I intend to employ force.

DOCTOR. Against a ghost?

INSPECTOR. I fully agree with the current theory, gentlemen, that Isabel's ghostly friend is none other than the young man whose hat was found on the edge of the lake. I differ only in a slight matter of interpretation. In my opinion that young man is still very much in the flesh.

MAYOR. Impossible!

INSPECTOR. We shall see. In a little while, the armed agents of the state will be waiting for him in this thicket.

MAYOR. What armed agents?

INSPECTOR. The game wardens?

MAYOR. Out of the question, Inspector. The trout season opened yesterday.

INSPECTOR. Well, then, the police?

DOCTOR. Sorry, Inspector. The police force is quar‧antined. Measles.

INSPECTOR. I don't mind if the ghost catches measles.

MAYOR. But the judge does. The judge will have nothing to do with any criminal that has measles. Sound justice requires sound criminals!

INSPECTOR. It's a good thing, Mr. Mayor, that I knew in advance to what an extent I could count on the cooperation of the local authorities in this case. Don't trouble. I am fully prepared to go ahead in spite of you.

MAYOR. *(Crossing to* INSPECTOR) You are not going to call out the army?

INSPECTOR. I have something more dependable than the army. As it happens, the one official in France who has no fear whatever of ghosts is a resident of this town.

MAYOR. You mean—the Public Executioner?

(SUPERVISOR *and* DOCTOR *rise.)*

INSPECTOR. Do you know him?

MAYOR. Nobody knows him. He never goes out.

INSPECTOR. I have written, offering him a fee of five thousand francs. I believe that will bring him out.

MAYOR. I'm afraid it will. *(Crosses Right Center.)*

INSPECTOR. I am waiting for him now. He will come armed.

MAYOR. But—what if the ghost is also armed?

SUPERVISOR. *(Crossing to* INSPECTOR*)* Inspector—before it's too late—please let me talk with Isabel—

INSPECTOR. Very well. Talk to her. She will be here in a moment. She's always punctual. *(He looks at his watch)* I will give you exactly five minutes. Now, where's this executioner? He appears to be late—*(Exits down Right with* MAYOR.*)*

DOCTOR. The Executioner is punctual only at dawn. *(Exits down Right.)*

(The SUPERVISOR *steps toward* ISABEL *as she enters Left.)*

SUPERVISOR. How lightly your foot falls, Miss Isabel. You walk on the seams of the forest like a skilful burglar who keeps the stairs from creaking by stepping just where the treads are nailed.

ISABEL. You have a gift for expression, Mr. Supervisor.

SUPERVISOR. I speak well when I have something to say. Not that I ever say what I mean. It's always something else by the time it comes out. But perhaps I don't make myself clear?

ISABEL. I understand that in speaking of the seams of the forest, you make use of a metaphor adapted to the female mentality. That's very considerate. I have been meaning to compliment you on the stand you have taken on the question of Madame Lambert.

SUPERVISOR. When I speak of Madame Lambert, I am not speaking of Madame Lambert.

ISABEL. I know. You are defending our sex, in general. It is very gallant and brave of you. Especially since you know how the Inspector hates us. Have you heard what that man is doing? He is employing spies. I am being watched day and night.

SUPERVISOR. The Administration thinks your interests are abnormal.

ISABEL. Are the interests of the Administration entirely normal? Are yours?

SUPERVISOR. Oh, by no means. It is clearly far from normal for anyone to be as lovely as you. And I find you very interesting, Miss Isabel.

ISABEL. Very prettily put. And surely not at all what you meant to say.

SUPERVISOR. Oh, Miss Isabel—this time—yes.

ISABEL. And in what way are my interests abnormal? Is it because I believe in spirits? That doesn't seem abnormal to me. What seems abnormal is the dull indifference of the living to everything that goes on outside of their lives. Or else we are all hypocrites—and the millions who say they believe in the afterlife, don't believe in anything of the sort.

SUPERVISOR. Do you really see ghosts, Miss Isabel?

ISABEL. So far only one.

SUPERVISOR. He's very handsome?

ISABEL. He's quite nice-looking.

SUPERVISOR. Young?

ISABEL. About thirty. I'd rather become ageless at thirty, wouldn't you, than with a long white beard?

SUPERVISOR. (A step in) Does he come near you? Do you let him touch you?

ISABEL. He never comes near me. He is too fragile. And he knows how clumsy we can be.

SUPERVISOR. But you look at him. You talk to him?

ISABEL. Of course.

SUPERVISOR. Do you really think that's wise, Miss Isabel?

ISABEL. Why not?

SUPERVISOR. Miss Isabel, one day you will hear a man—a living man—asking you to be his wife. What will you answer?

ISABEL. That depends a little, doesn't it? (Crosses Right and sits on stump.)

SUPERVISOR. If I understand you, Miss Isabel, you

intend to continue your relations with this ghost? And with others too, perhaps?

ISABEL. Naturally. One likes to extend one's circle of acquaintances as far as possible.

SUPERVISOR. But if these acquaintances should interefere with one's life?

ISABEL. Why should they? That idle hour of the day during which a wife invites her soul—her memories, her hopes, perhaps even her lover—what harm if she devotes it to an invisible friend?

SUPERVISOR. Your husband may not like this invisible friend.

ISABEL. So many invisible things come between a husband and a wife—do you think one more will matter?

SUPERVISOR. This one.

ISABEL. Why should it?

SUPERVISOR. Because the one thing we know about ghosts, Miss Isabel, is they are extremely devoted. It's doubtless a consequence of their lack of regular employment. *(Steps in)* You must admit it would be disconcerting to have a ghostly rival materialize in the midst of one's most intimate moments.

ISABEL. A ghostly rival?

SUPERVISOR. Beware, Miss Isabel. Beware of these phantoms who prowl around young girls. Their intentions are not honorable. We know their little game. They begin by appealing to your sympathy, to your softness. They're helpless and lonely, so they say. What they want is, little by little, for their own dark purposes, to cut you off from the rest of humanity, to lead you step by step away from those who have a healthy human interest in neckties and petticoats and bread and cheese. It's happening to you now, Isabel. For heaven's sake, take care!

ISABEL. Dear Supervisor, please try to understand. Of all the multitude of the dead, my ghost is the only one who has been able to penetrate our sphere far enough to establish communication. I know he is not the only one who has tried. Sometimes I feel that in the vast sea of the dead, powerful currents are flowing toward me. I feel the pressure of their longing as it merges with mine, and I know that through me at last they will find a way to flow back into the world of the living.

SUPERVISOR. Isabel—this is madness!

ISABEL. Every child knows that the void beyond life is peopled with figures. The darkness that hems us about is only our dullness. If we stretch a hand through this darkness a thousand hands stretch forth in answer. Already one has grasped mine in trust and friendship. Why should I let it go?

SUPERVISOR. Isabel, Isabel, do you know what you are doing? In the name of God, stay away from the bounds of life, its limits. Its glory is to be brief and full between two voids. Its miracle is to be something balanced firmly upon nothing. But let a single drop of nothingness fall into it, and the result may be disastrous. That is why every mortal is pledged from his birth to guard the frontiers of existence. Open the gate, be it ever so slightly, and you destroy us all.

ISABEL. *(Rises, crossing to Left Center)* Or save you all.

SUPERVISOR. Once the gate of death is open, who knows what horror may surge through?

ISABEL. Death holds no horrors. It is simply the ultimate horror of life. It's for our sake, not for theirs that I wish the dead to return. We need them desperately.

SUPERVISOR. What in the world for?

ISABEL. You asked me a moment ago what I would say to the man who one day would want to take me in his arms. I will tell you. If it is in order to shut out this new world that calls me, if it is to close my mouth with his lips, and my eyes with his kisses, to make yet another of these double-backed beasts that labor to propagate the wretched race of men—no. I won't have him, no matter how beautiful he is. If you know this man, give him my answer. And now, good-bye.

SUPERVISOR. Miss Isabel—whatever you do, I beg of you—don't meet the ghost tonight.

ISABEL. And why not tonight?

SUPERVISOR. Because the Inspector has set a trap for him.

ISABEL. He doesn't fear the Inspector's traps. Please go now.

SUPERVISOR. I'm staying here.

ISABEL. Why?

SUPERVISOR. I want to see this ghost.

ISABEL. You will never see him.

SUPERVISOR. I will not only see him, I will unmask him once and for all. I will show you how genuine this ghost is—

ISABEL. Please do. There he is.

SUPERVISOR. Where?

ISABEL. Right behind you—see? You seem to amuse him. He's smiling.

SUPERVISOR. Isabel, don't joke about this. The Inspector is already posting his men. They have orders to capture your ghost dead or alive.

ISABEL. Do you think they will know which is which? —Oh, there's the moon, see, Mr. Supervisor—genuine silver. See? The hallmark? *(She disappears off Left, laughing.)*

(The SUPERVISOR *is still listening to her laughter when the* INSPECTOR, *the* MAYOR *and the* DOCTOR *walk in Right.)*

INSPECTOR. *(Crossing to Center)* Well, dear boy— you don't have the look of a successful man.

SUPERVISOR. I'll try again tomorrow.

INSPECTOR. Good idea. In the meantime, be so good as to get your class together. It's getting dark. It's time they were in bed. *(The* SUPERVISOR *nods and walks off down Right into the woods. The* INSPECTOR *beckons to someone off stage.* DOCTOR *goes down Left;* MAYOR *down Right.)* All right, boys. (EXECUTIONERS *enter Right to Left of stump.)* Now. What's all this about? Which of you is the executioner?

FIRST EXECUTIONER. I am.

INSPECTOR. Then who are you?

SECOND EXECUTIONER. The executioner.

INSPECTOR. One of you is obviously lying.

FIRST EXECUTIONER. Not me, sir.

SECOND EXECUTIONER. Not me.

INSPECTOR. Well, we'll soon find out. Let's have a look at your papers. Hm—Profession: Cornetist. Now, what makes you think you're an executioner?

FIRST EXECUTIONER. You know the police never register our real profession, Inspector. They always put us down as musicians.

SECOND EXECUTIONER. That's correct, Inspector. I'm down as a contra-bassoon.

INSPECTOR. Empty your pockets, both of you. Mr. Mayor, inspect their belongings. *(Steps Left.)*

MAYOR. *(To Right of* FIRST EXECUTIONER) This one has a patent corkscrew, three cigarettes, five francs and a toothpick.

INSPECTOR. Perfectly normal.

MAYOR. *(Crossing to Left of* SECOND EXECU-TIONER. *Looking at the other's effects)* A fountain pen, two cough drops, a rubber band and a broken comb. Some change and a key. *(Crosses Left below log.)*

INSPECTOR. Search any man suddenly and that's what you find. Well? Well, which is the executioner?

MAYOR. It should be perfectly easy to tell an executioner from an ordinary person.

INSPECTOR. Really? Let's see you do it.

MAYOR. Why—.

DOCTOR. They say a dog always bristles when he sees an executioner. All we have to do is find a dog—

INSPECTOR. Where do you expect me all of a sudden to find a dog?

MAYOR. I have it! Why not examine them on the elements of their profession? *(Sits on log.)*

INSPECTOR. *(Crossing Left)* That's an idea. You— of what material is the guillotine constructed? *(Sits on log.)*

FIRST EXECUTIONER. Of oak. Except for the runners—

SECOND EXECUTIONER. Which are always made of teak.

INSPECTOR. Hm. What did Madame Du Barry say when she mounted the scaffold? You?

FIRST EXECUTIONER. She said, "Just a moment, Mr. Executioner, just a little moment more."

INSPECTOR. Who was it said to the headsman, "Lend me a hand up the ladder, please. As for coming down, I'll shift for myelf?"—You.

SECOND EXECUTIONER. Sir Thomas More. 1535.

INSPECTOR. This is a waste of time. You there— what was the law of January 4th, 1847?

FIRST EXECUTIONER. That's the statute in which condemned persons are reminded that an execution is a solemn occasion, and that consequently jokes and witticisms are prohibited on the scaffold.

MAYOR. Can you sing the "Executioner's Song"?

FIRST EXECUTIONER. Which one?

INSPECTOR. Are there more than one?

SECOND EXECUTIONER. There are dozens. "The Headsman with the Golden Hair"?

FIRST EXECUTIONER. "The Hangman's Reel"?

SECOND EXECUTIONER. "My Head Is in the Clouds."

MAYOR. "The Headsman with the Golden Hair."

FIRST EXECUTIONER. *(Sings)*
>When I set up my guillotine
>Upon the village square,
>The dawn pours rosy brilliantine
>Upon my golden hair.

SECOND EXECUTIONER. *(Taking up the tune)*
>No trace of Houbigant for Men
>No fragrance of Chanel

Clings to my golden ringlets when
I greet my clientele.

DUO.

My shirt is starched, my cuffs are white,
My blade gleams in the morning light,
Can I be blamed if people stare
And say, what lovely golden hair?

INSPECTOR. *(Rising)* The devil take the examination!
If the executioner insists on being twins, he'll just
have to divide the fee with himself.

FIRST EXECUTIONER. Fair enough.

SECOND EXECUTIONER. All right.

INSPECTOR. Are you armed? *(They nod, and pull
out their pistols.* MAYOR *rises.)* These are your in-
structions: you will be posted in this thicket. You will
keep a sharp lookout.

FIRST EXECUTIONER. Will there be much waiting?
If I stay up after midnight, I always get the shakes—.

INSPECTOR. It will all be over in a few minutes. First
you will see a young girl—

SECOND EXECUTIONER. Oh—

INSPECTOR. Then a young man.

FIRST EXECUTIONER. Ah—

INSPECTOR. You will permit them to talk together a
minute or so.

SECOND EXECUTIONER. Can we listen to what they
say?

INSPECTOR. You may. The man will sit here—the
woman there. Take careful aim at the man. And at a
given signal, fire.

FIRST EXECUTIONER. To kill?

INSPECTOR. The man is wanted for murder and has
been evading arrest. The government gives you full
authority to kill him.

SECOND EXECUTIONER. What's the signal?

INSPECTOR. Whatever you agree on.

FIRST EXECUTIONER. Obelisk?

INSPECTOR. Why obelisk?

SECOND EXECUTIONER. That's the word we always

use in the trade as a signal to spring the machine. Obelisk—bang! It's a good clear word you can't mistake.

FIRST EXECUTIONER. All right, then. The minute the man says obelisk, we shoot.

INSPECTOR. You may have to wait in these bushes several years before it occurs to the man to say obelisk. But if you're looking for a word, there is one he is certain to use within the next two minutes.

MAYOR. What word is that?

INSPECTOR. Alive.

FIRST EXECUTIONER. All right. The minute he says alive, we fire.

SECOND EXECUTIONER. Alive—bang!

DOCTOR. *(Crossing in)* Hadn't you better tell them what it is they're going to shoot?

INSPECTOR. Ever hear of Axel Petersen?

FIRST EXECUTIONER. The Headsman of Göteborg?

SECOND EXECUTIONER. The one who beheaded the ghost?

INSPECTOR. That's it. And now you understand.

FIRST EXECUTIONER. What do you mean? Is this murderer a ghost?

INSPECTOR. So he says. Do you mind?

SECOND EXECUTIONER. It's all the same to us.

INSPECTOR. Come along, then. *(On the way to stump to* DOCTOR, *who has just taken some objects out of his pocket)* What's that you've got?

DOCTOR. My pitch-pipes. My tuning fork.

INSPECTOR. What are they for?

DOCTOR. The transition.

INSPECTOR. Eh?

DOCTOR. We are about to pass from the minor into the major.

INSPECTOR. Mm-hm. *(Tapping his forehead)* Bit touched.

(He winks at the MAYOR *and walks off Right with the* EXECUTIONERS.)*

DOCTOR. *(Looking at his pipes)* I was worried. I thought I'd lost them. But here they are.

MAYOR. *(Taking them absently)* Do you realize what is about to happen?

DOCTOR. I much prefer this type that you blow—don't blow it—to these things that look like curling irons.

MAYOR. *(Crossing to Right Center)* Doctor—a life is at stake!

DOCTOR. I looked everywhere for them. And all the time they were here in my pocket. If two coppers had slipped into the lining of my coat, I'd have jingled like a junk cart. And here was all the music in the world, and it didn't make a sound. Well, at any rate, we're saved.

MAYOR. Are you counting on this whistle to protect Isabel?

DOCTOR. My dear friend, do you really think Isabel needs our protection?

MAYOR. Doesn't she?

DOCTOR. No. At this moment the entire universe is protecting Isabel. If a mountain should fall upon Isabel, it wouldn't harm a hair of her head. Nature takes care of everything. The only question with us in a case like this is whether or not we are in tune with nature. If we are, we're all right. And if not, I have my pitch-pipes.

MAYOR. Do you think you can tune Nature like a piano?

DOCTOR. Oh no. Like a choir.

MAYOR. *(He crosses to exit Right)* These mysteries are beyond me. I'm going to try and reason with the Inspector. In the meantime, I leave you alone with Nature.

DOCTOR. Thank you.

MAYOR. *(Turning)* You're quite certain Isabel is in no danger?

DOCTOR. Quite certain.

MAYOR. What about us?

DOCTOR. Don't worry. On a right note a man is as safe in a whirlwind as in a church. *(The* MAYOR *exits. The* DOCTOR *holds up his hand)* Attention, please.

(He blows into his pipe. Nature takes his pitch and all of it resounds in a chord of complete harmony. He nods, satisfied, and tiptoes out Right. As he does so, ISABEL *enters down Left, crosses to stump and sits. The* GHOST *enters down Left to above log.)*

GHOST. Did I keep you waiting?

ISABEL. If I were a phantom, I think I should move very slowly in the twilight. I should pause, here to enfold a singing bird in my substance, there to mingle for a moment with a passing breeze—and sometimes, I should melt utterly into the fragrance of a bush of honeysuckle. I'm afraid that once free of this shell of flesh, I should always be late for appointments.

GHOST. *(Steps in)* Then you forgive me?

ISABEL. *(Rising; to Center)* But you have come alone again. Oh, couldn't you have got someone to come with you just this once?

GHOST. No.

ISABEL. *(Steps in)* We thought yesterday that the kind of sound that might wake them would be a sort of wailing scream—like the screech of a locomotive in the middle of the night. Did you try that?

GHOST. Yes.

ISABEL. And didn't you find then that, one by one, innumerable voices rose up to echo yours?

GHOST. No.

ISABEL. They must sleep very deeply, the dead.

GHOST. Compared with the sleep of the dead, the sleep of the living is moonlight sparkling on the water.

ISABEL. Will it always be like that?

GHOST. I'm afraid so.

ISABEL. Then you think there's no hope at all?

GHOST. I'm afraid not.

ISABEL. That can't be. I know, with some people when they die, it's complete. They sink into the void like stones. But there are others who go into death as if it were an expedition. When they go, you want to wave a handkerchief and wish them luck. You can't tell me that they won't waken when they're called.

GHOST. I have seen no one of that sort.

ISABEL. But what about you? Are you content to spend the rest of eternity haunting a lake?

GHOST. Perhaps it's all I'm good for.

ISABEL. I won't let you say that. You know it's not true.

GHOST. Oh, why don't I just vanish!

ISABEL. Because you can't. I've caught you in my trap.

GHOST. Trap?

ISABEL. I have a ghost-trap in my room. Didn't you know?

GHOST. Are you a sorceress?

ISABEL. *(Crossing to below log)* My sorcery is very simple. For a long time, I wondered what would be most likely to attract the dead. I decided it wouldn't be their friends or their books or anything of that sort —it would be something quite modest and homely. Perhaps a little pattern of light and shade—the glitter of a doorknob, the flash of a white petal, the pink nose of a cat—a little mosaic of living things. That would be irresistible, I thought, to a soul that was steeped in darkness. And so—

GHOST. *(Sitting on log)* And so—?

ISABEL. I've arranged my room very cleverly. Superficially, it's just a room for a living girl—a girl living in the provinces, to be exact. But look carefully, and you will see that everything is calculated to the last detail. The curve of a pot, the surface of a table—by day they catch the sun; by night, the lamplight or the moon—the little pattern is always there, marking a spot of warmth in the coldness of the universe. That's the extent of my sorcery. And that is why I wasn't in

the least surprised the night I saw your face peering
in at my window as I brushed my hair. You were en-
tranced, I could see. You were caught.

GHOST. Yes. I was caught. And again I'm caught—

ISABEL. By what?

GHOST. Another of your patterns. Your voice, your
face, but most of all your spirit—a spirit so generous
and innocent that I am sure it could harbor not the
faintest suspicion that all this while I might be deceiv-
ing you cruelly—that I might be, in fact, no ghost at
all, but—very much—

ISABEL. What?

GHOST. Alive!

*(Two SHOTS ring out. ISABEL rises; runs down
Left. The GHOST rises and falls behind log. The
INSPECTOR, the MAYOR, the DOCTOR, the EXECU-
TIONERS run in. DOCTOR and MAYOR from down
Right, DOCTOR to GHOST, MAYOR to below log.
INSPECTOR up Center. EXECUTIONERS to above
stump.)*

MAYOR. What is that? On the ground?

INSPECTOR. Look and see.

DOCTOR. *(Beside the body)* Poor chap!

MAYOR. Is he dead?

(DOCTOR rises; gestures; crosses to Left Center.)

INSPECTOR. A make-believe ghost. A genuine corpse.

MAYOR. *(Taking ISABEL in his arms)* My poor child!
Oh, what have you done, you wretches?

INSPECTOR. You might thank them. With two shots,
they have rid society of a criminal, the girl of an obses-
sion, and the town of a ghost.

MAYOR. But nobody really believed it was a ghost.
What harm would it have done to let her preserve her
illusion?

INSPECTOR. A good deal of harm. This girl has upset the whole community. She must be made to see what her ghost really was—not only a criminal, but a cheat and a liar.

MAYOR. Come, my little Isabel—this poor boy has paid his debt to society in full. Forgive him.

DOCTOR. It's too late for that. His heart has stopped beating.

INSPECTOR. It would be troublesome if it hadn't. Since he's dead.

DOCTOR. But forgive us, Isabel. And you, poor ghost—we beg your pardon!

INSPECTOR. Are you mad? What are you apologizing for?

DOCTOR. *(Still kneeling beside the corpse)* I apologize because in this world the truth is always vulgar.

(But at this moment a spirit rises from the ground where the dead man is lying. He is exactly like the GHOST, *point for point, but he has authenticity. And as they see the apparition, one after the other, they realize beyond doubt that this time it is a ghost.* ISABEL *and the* MAYOR, *who were about to leave, stop in their tracks. The* EXECUTIONERS *look up with open mouths. Only the* DOCTOR *sees nothing.)*

DOCTOR. I apologize because life has no spirit, and death no dignity. Because the illusions of youth are illusions, and age is generous only in destruction. I apologize because in this world the Inspector is always right, and the spectre is false.

(By now the GHOST *has risen to its full height.)*

FIRST EXECUTIONER. Inspector—
SECOND EXECUTIONER. Inspector—
INSPECTOR. There seems to be something wrong with my eyes. There's surely nothing there?
ISABEL. *(In exaltation)* Yes. There is.

MAYOR. Yes. There is.

DOCTOR. *(Looking up)* Yes. There is.

INSPECTOR. *(A step Right)* It's a birch tree—in the moonlight. And in our excitement—

MAYOR. No, it isn't.

DOCTOR. No, it isn't.

ISABEL. No, it isn't.

(GHOST *crosses to Left Center at end of log.)*

THE EXECUTIONERS. Look out. It's moving toward us!

INSPECTOR. Be calm, my children. Be calm. It's a phenomenon—perfectly well-known phenomenon. It's called a mirage. They're common in Africa. Do you see it upside down, Doctor, or straight?

MAYOR. Very straight.

DOCTOR. His head is high—

ISABEL. Yes.

INSPECTOR. It's a will of the wisp. It's nothing but marsh gas. It's an effect of static electricity in the evening mist—a halo. The slightest breath will dissipate it. I'll show you. *(Crosses to Center. Blows hard. The* GHOST *grows brighter. Crosses Right)* Well, I hope this crazy girl is happy now that her hallucinations—have reached the upper levels of the administration. Of course, the illusion is only visual—

GHOST. Until tomorrow, Isabel!

INSPECTOR. What?

GHOST. Tomorrow at six, Isabel! I will come to your home, Isabel! And this time, I will come with the others, Isabel! With all the others! *(He vanishes up Right.)*

(EXECUTIONERS *cross to back of log.)*

INSPECTOR. I'm not feeling well. Doctor—if you don't mind—

DOCTOR. Get him away from here. He's had a bad shock. *(To* ISABEL*)* Go, my child. It's all over.

ISABEL. For today. But tomorrow—

GHOST. *(Reappearing for an instant)* Tomorrow, Isabel. Tomorrow.

(The INSPECTOR *walks off Right, between* ISABEL *and the* MAYOR. *The* DOCTOR *and the* TWO EXECU-TIONERS *busy themselves about the body. A murmur of girls' VOICES is heard offstage, and the* SUPERVISOR *comes in Right.)*

SUPERVISOR. We heard shots. Has something happened?

DOCTOR. Yes. Something has happened. Your moment has come.

SUPERVISOR. Which one? I have so many.

DOCTOR. The moment when you must fight your rival for the woman you love.

SUPERVISOR. I have a rival?

(The DOCTOR *points to the body which the* EXECU-TIONERS *have taken up and are about to carry off.)*

SUPERVISOR. The ghost?

(The DOCTOR *nods gravely. The* GIRLS *are heard plainly now and their lights flicker off Right amid the foliage. The* EXECUTIONERS *have carried the body off Left.)*

DENISE. Here he is!   *(WARN Curtain.)*

DOCTOR. *(He takes the* SUPERVISOR's *arm)* Listen carefully, my boy. What has happened tonight is something so important, so extraordinary that—

DENISE. *(Appears)* Here they are!

GILBERTE. Wait for us!

DAISY. What's happened?

(All the GIRLS run in.)

DOCTOR. Better get them home now. I'll talk to you later. *(He follows the EXECUTIONERS.)*

SUPERVISOR. *(Checking over his class, absently)* Where's Lucy?

THE GIRLS. Lucy! Lucy!

(LUCY runs in Right.)

SUPERVISOR. Do you mind telling me why you always lag behind?

LUCY. Because I was looking for glow-worms with my flashlight.

SUPERVISOR. That's silly. Nobody looks for glow-worms with a flashlight.

(They begin to move off Left.)

LUCY. Because I lost my garter.

SUPERVISOR. It's in your hand. You were using it for a sling.

LUCY. Because—

SUPERVISOR. Because what?

(Exit Left. All the GIRLS follow him. Only LUCY remains behind.)

LUCY. Because— *(She flings her beret high into the air.)*

SUPERVISOR. *(Offstage)* Lucy!

THE GIRLS. *(Offstage)* Lucy! Lucy! Lucy! Lucy!

LUCY. Because I love to be alone at night in the forest!

CURTAIN

ACT THREE

SCENE: ISABEL'S *room. It has a balcony in rear with French windows through which the city square is visible. There are doors Right and Left. A table and chair down Right; a chest above the Right door; a table Right of French window, an armoire Left of it. A chair above Left door and a table below it. A sofa Left Center. The military BAND is tuning up in the distance. There are faint flourishes, ariettes, and ruffles on the DRUMS.*

Late afternoon. The next day.

AT RISE: *There is a rattling of KEYS off Right. The hall door Right opens. The* INSPECTOR *and* GIRLS *enter on tiptoe. The* MAYOR *follows them.* INSPECTOR *goes to window;* GIRLS *look around.*

MAYOR. *(Crossing to chair Right of table)* I hope you realize that this constitutes breaking and entering.

INSPECTOR. *(To down Right of sofa)* And how else do you expect to enter a young girl's room at your age? What time is it?

MAYOR. By the sun, I'd say 5:30.

INSPECTOR. I doubt if ghosts go by the sun.

MAYOR. If they go by my watch, it's 5:38.

INSPECTOR. That gives us exactly twenty-two minutes. The ghost said he'd come at six with the others. There's just time to man our defenses.

(DAISY, IRENE, GILBERTE *at door Right;* VIOLA, LUCY, DENISE *at door Left.)*

MAYOR. What defenses?

INSPECTOR. Mr. Mayor, at this historic moment when humanity is faced with the most terrible invasion it has ever known, the honor of manning the outposts falls to us. I hope you are fully aware of the responsibility.

MAYOR. Inspector—

INSPECTOR. The enemy is in its trenches, massed for attack.

MAYOR. Where? In the cemetery?

INSPECTOR. No. In the beyond.

MAYOR. So at last, you have come to believe in spirits!

INSPECTOR. Mr. Mayor, I always believe in the enemies of France.

MAYOR. What if Isabel finds us here?

INSPECTOR. *(Crosses up Center)* She won't. I have had the town clock set back an hour. Furthermore, I am posting Gilberte at the window. (GILBERTE *goes up to windows.*) Gilberte! If you see anything come this way, you will report immediately.

GILBERTE. *(At the window)* I see the Mangebois sisters coming. Shall I report them?

INSPECTOR. Report everything.

GILBERTE. They've stopped.

INSPECTOR. Good. And now—

GILBERTE. The druggist's poodle is coming.

MAYOR. Inspector, do you mind telling me what we have come to do here?

INSPECTOR. We have come to exorcise a ghost.

MAYOR. You mean with bell, book and candle? Do you have a priest?

INSPECTOR. *(A step Right)* Do you expect me to appeal from one superstition to another? I am going to exorcise this ghost in my official capacity as administrative head of the sub-prefecture.

MAYOR. You think the ghost will be impressed?

INSPECTOR. Ghosts are impressed by any sort of rubbish. For hundreds of years the church has scared

them off simply by telling them to go away in Latin.
(Crosses and sits on sofa) I have no doubt that the
official adjuration which I composed this morning will
be much more effective. At least, they will know what
I am saying.

GILBERTE. You want me to report trees too?

INSPECTOR. Trees don't move, silly.

GILBERTE. *(Retreating from window step by step in
awe)* And yet— I think— And yet— I think—

INSPECTOR. You may relieve Gilberte, Viola. She's
getting nervous.

MAYOR. I don't know that I exactly blame her.

INSPECTOR. Are you nervous too?

MAYOR. *(Rising)* To tell the truth, I'm in a perfect
sweat. The more so as with this hocus-pocus you're
keeping me from the drawing of the civic lottery, at
which I invariably preside.

INSPECTOR. Is this a time to worry about lotteries?

MAYOR. Well, it's a very important civic function.

INSPECTOR. And what we are doing here is not an
important civic function, I suppose! Has it not yet
dawned upon you, Mr. Mayor, that what we are involved in is not merely of local or national or even
international importance, but absolutely universal in
its consequences?

MAYOR. Are you serious? *(Sits.)*

INSPECTOR. *(Crossing to Right Center)* Do you realize what it would mean to France if the inhabitants of
the other world were permitted to colonize this district? *(Sits Left of table)* I say nothing of their influence on the local community, which is already mad.
But take notice that these ghosts would not be aliens.
They would be natives of France, and therefore en-
titled to all the rights and privileges of citizens, including the right to vote. And when you stop to think
that the dead of this district outnumber the living in
astronomical proportion—you can see what the consequences might be. Within five years, with perfect
legality, they could capture any electoral post in the

nation. The president of the Republic would be a ghost, the prime minister would be a ghost, the members of the high court, all ghosts—

MAYOR. You think we would notice any difference?

INSPECTOR. As ghosts don't eat, and require neither clothing nor shelter, they would hardly understand our interest in the material things of life. In a short time, the human race, vastly outnumbered everywhere, would be reduced to the level of slaves. *(Rises, crosses to Center)* The death-certificate would replace the passport; wherever one turned one would be confronted with phantoms, hordes of phantoms, clouds of phantoms—good heavens, we should have to plow our way through phantoms like ships in a fog—! *(Sits on sofa.)*

MAYOR. Dear me!

INSPECTOR. It's a good thing I'm here.

MAYOR. *(Rising)* Inspector, you have opened my eyes! Under these circumstances, no one could count on a moment's privacy.

INSPECTOR. Aha! So you begin to see?

MAYOR. *(Crosses to Right of sofa)* I have but one real passion in life: I collect stamps. I specialize in imperforate Antilles of the period 1855-1870; for the past twenty years I have spent my evenings delightfully, turning over the pages of my album in the exquisite solitude of my study. People think I am studying official papers. I lock the door.

INSPECTOR. Wise precaution.

MAYOR. Every man has his secret vice, Inspector.

INSPECTOR. Well?

MAYOR. Well, under the uncomprehending stare of one's assembled ancestors, the Merovingians, say, or the ancient Gauls, one might feel a trifle embarrassed, don't you think, playing at my age with bits of colored paper?

INSPECTOR. It's entirely possible.

MAYOR. Naturally, when I say Antilles, I include the Bahamas, Trinidad and even Nassau—but still— *(He shakes his head.)*

(The sounds of the BAND offstage fade out completely.)

INSPECTOR. *(Rises; crosses Right Center with MAYOR)* I take it you agree, then, that these phantoms who propose to populate the district must be considered an undesirable element?

VIOLA. The houses are moving, Inspector—the houses!

INSPECTOR. *(Crossing up Center)* Houses don't move, silly.

VIOLA. And yet— I think— And yet— I think—

INSPECTOR. Daisy, you go to the window. *(Crosses down Center)* Well?

(DAISY and VIOLA change positions.)

MAYOR. The only safeguard of human dignity—the door and the doorlatch—would vanish forever!

INSPECTOR. And the windowshade. *(Crosses to below sofa)* Very well, then. *(MAYOR crosses below sofa.)* The little ceremony which you are about to witness is designed to preserve to our posterity these monuments of human ingenuity—together with some other trifles, such as law and order and a living wage. In order to insure the solemnity of the occasion, I wired the Prefect and the Minister of Public Safety to be present as representatives of the human race. For some reason, they have sent their regrets. I shall therefore proceed with the company at my disposal—that is to say, the Mayor and the Sixth Grade. Children, form a circle. *(The GIRLS form a semi-circle at Center.)* As I read, you will repeat after me in chorus the last word of every important sentence. That should make a proper ceremonial effect.

THE GIRLS. Effect.

INSPECTOR. Just a moment. *(He takes a document from his pocket and unfolds it with solemnity. He puts on his spectacles. The military BAND crashes suddenly into a slow march)* Spirits! Ghosts! Phantoms! Powers of darkness! I address you in the name of humanity!

THE GIRLS. Humanity.

INSPECTOR. What is humanity? Humanity is a super-human enterprise!

THE GIRLS. Enterprise.

INSPECTOR. The purpose of which is to distinguish the race of man from the hodge-podge of the infinite, by means of the invincible forces of government and science.

THE GIRLS. And science.

INSPECTOR. Government defines the physical aspects of man by means of the printed form, so that for every man in the flesh there is an exactly corresponding man on paper. In this way, man becomes a function of the State.

THE GIRLS. The State.

INSPECTOR. Science, on the other hand, liberates the spirit of man from the infinite by means of material rewards. Thus, each time that man succeeds in casting off one of the spiritual husks of his being, Science provides him with an exact equivalent in the world of matter. When in the eighteenth century, man ceased to believe in the fire and smoke of hell, Science provided him with immediate compensation in the form of steam and gas.

THE GIRLS. Gas.

INSPECTOR. When he ceased any longer to heed the words of the seers and the prophets, Science lovingly brought forth the Radio Comment—

THE GIRLS. —tator.

INSPECTOR. In place of revelation, he now has—

THE GIRLS. Journalism.

INSPECTOR. So that now, for the worship of the Infinite, he is able at last to substitute the worship of—

THE GIRLS. The Atom.

INSPECTOR. *(Severely)* His Reason. Thus, through the ages, Science brushes away the cobwebs of superstition, and lays bare the walls of being until every corner of the universe is explored, explained and flooded with—

THE GIRLS. Artificial illumination.

INSPECTOR. With light! Therefore, now, Spirits of Darkness, in the name of Government, of Science, and of their servant, Humanity, whose every interest is opposed to yours, I declare you obsolete, useless and undesirable, and you are hereby forbidden to enter this jurisdiction on any pretext whatever, under the penalties provided for cases of illegal immigration, Law of June 13th, 1897, Paragraph 8, Section 2. In witness whereof—

DAISY. (Coming from window to Center) Here they come!

(The BAND stops suddenly in the middle of a measure, and on a false note. GIRLS, except DAISY, run to Left door.)

INSPECTOR. Who?
DAISY. The Ghosts! The Ghosts!
INSPECTOR. What? (He walks out Left quickly.)

(DAISY to above sofa.)

MAYOR. (To above sofa) Come, children, this is no place for you.

DAISY. It's not the ghosts. I was only joking. It's Miss Isabel and the Doctor.

MAYOR. (Pushing LUCY Left) Out with you. This way—quick.

(They run out through the door, Left. ISABEL and the DOCTOR come in, Right. ISABEL to up Left Center; DOCTOR to Center.)

ISABEL. I'm terribly grateful. If I hadn't met you, I'd certainly have been late.

DOCTOR. The town clock must have stopped. It's nearly six.

ISABEL. Do you think he will really come here?

DOCTOR. I think so.

ISABEL. I don't see why he should. He's not my ghost any more. He's everybody's ghost. They're all waiting for him—the whole town. Perhaps the whole world. *(Crosses down to Right of sofa.)*

DOCTOR. I believe he will come here.

ISABEL. Why?

DOCTOR. Because he needs you.

ISABEL. Why should he need me? What will he want of me?

DOCTOR. I don't know. But I think he will want you to join him.

ISABEL. In death?

DOCTOR. Perhaps.

ISABEL. Couldn't I be just as useful—even more useful—alive?

DOCTOR. To us, yes. But to him—?

ISABEL. You'll stay with me, won't you?

DOCTOR. Are you afraid to see him alone?

ISABEL. I don't know. I don't know. Please stay. Please?

DOCTOR. If you wish.

(They BOTH walk slowly to the window. The town CLOCK strikes five. There is a KNOCK on the door. They don't move. Another KNOCK. The DOCTOR turns. The door Right swings open.)

ISABEL. Has he come? (SUPERVISOR *enters Right.)*

DOCTOR. Yes. *(With a smile)* And I think I'll leave you alone with him, after all, my dear.

ISABEL. *(Looking at the* SUPERVISOR, *who is still in the doorway)* Oh.

DOCTOR. Goodbye.

ISABEL. *(Tenderly)* Goodbye. Goodbye, dear Doctor.

(She takes a step forward. The SUPERVISOR *enters. The* DOCTOR *nods as he passes him and goes out, Right, shutting the door. The* SUPERVISOR *looks pale and very formal. He stands silent a moment, dressed in his Sunday best—black jacket, striped trousers, chamois gloves. He has a bowler hat in his right hand, a gold-headed stick in his left.* ISABEL *gazes at him in astonishment. The military* BAND, *much fainter now, strikes up a slow and stately waltz.)*

SUPERVISOR. *(Crosses above table to Center)* Not a word, if you please.

ISABEL. I don't know what to say.

SUPERVISOR. Don't say anything. Just listen.

ISABEL. Do you mind if I look?

SUPERVISOR. That is permitted. In fact, please do.

ISABEL. You look so grand.

SUPERVISOR. Don't poke fun at my finery. It is all that sustains me at the moment. Except the thought of those who should be wearing it. They would certainly be here with me, if they were alive. As it is, let me present—my grandfather: his cane. My great-uncle: his watch and chain. My father: his hat. My Uncle Albert: his gloves. The rest is myself.

ISABEL. I am delighted to meet you all. Please sit down. *(Sits on sofa.)*

SUPERVISOR. *(To above chair Left of table)* May I stow my relatives in this chair? There's quite a lot of them. *(He puts down his hat, stick and gloves.)*

ISABEL. And to what am I indebted for the pleasure of receiving your family on this occasion?

SUPERVISOR. *(Crosses to Center)* You haven't guessed? *(He bows ceremonially)* We have come for the purpose of asking your hand in marriage, Mademoiselle.

ISABEL. But, really—!

SUPERVISOR. Not a word, if you please. We ask you for your hand; not for your answer. We ask you, by withholding your answer until tomorrow, to give me the happiest day of my life—a day during which I can say to myself that at last I have asked you, and as yet you have not refused. A day in which I am permitted to think that you may be a little touched, perhaps, by the thought that there is someone, however unworthy, who lives only for you. Someone, *(To above chair again)* incidently, called Robert—my father *(He takes up the gloves)* will have told you my name by now. Someone who is brave, honest, concientious, reliable— and even modest. For my grandfather— *(He takes up the cane)* —can hardly be expected to spare you even the least of my virtues. Someone who—come, Uncle Albert— *(He takes his hat)* has the honor to wish you good day, Mademoiselle. Until tomorrow. *(Goes up Right.)*

ISABEL. No, no. Don't go. Only—you come at such a moment!

SUPERVISOR. *(Steps in up Right Center)* I chose the moment deliberately. It is his moment. And therefore the logical time for me to offer you another road to the other world. *(Crosses Center.)*

ISABEL. What road is that? Are there more than one?

SUPERVISOR. There is a road which leads slowly, easily, but very surely, to death.

ISABEL. What road?

SUPERVISOR. Life.

ISABEL. Life with you?

SUPERVISOR. That's not the important thing. I, as an individual, don't count for much in this affair. What I offer you is not so much life with me, as life with a government employee. I offer you a career which ends quite pleasantly in the other world. I suppose I go with it.—But perhaps you don't understand me? *(Crosses Right Center.)*

ISABEL. I think perhaps I do.

SUPERVISOR. In the civil service, the advances are regular and statutory. We move from post to post, from year to year, with the smoothness of time. We are borne as on a gentle stream from increment to increment, from youth to age, from age to death—without break and without transition.

ISABEL. It doesn't sound so terribly exciting.

SUPERVISOR. Oh, it is immensely exciting. It is all sheer poetry.

ISABEL. Really? I wish you'd explain that to me. You find it all sheer poetry in the Bureau of Weights and Measures?

SUPERVISOR. (*Sits beside her and takes her hand*) I'll give you an example. Say, I am checking the volume of the barrels in a distillery. The moment I am bored— I transform these liters into gallons, and in a twinkling, I am in America. On the way home, I have ten kilometers to travel. If I put it into versts, I am in Russia; in parasangs, in Persia; in fathoms, I am under the sea.

ISABEL. Oh.

SUPERVISOR. I check a load of grain in hins—the owner becomes an ancient Hebrew; in talents—a Roman; in drachmae—a Greek. I take a height in cubits —I am with Cleopatra; in ells, with Alfred the Great.

ISABEL. You *are* a poet, aren't you?

SUPERVISOR. The poetry of a life like mine is surpassed only by its continual surprises—!

ISABEL. Its surprises? Do you have surprises in the Weights and Measures? I should like to understand that. Because, frankly, surprises are what I love best of all in life.

SUPERVISOR. We have the most delightful, the most exquisite surprises. You know, of course, Miss Isabel, that in my bureau we have to change posts every three years—.

ISABEL. It seems rather long to be in one place.

SUPERVISOR. But at the very beginning of each assignment, we are given the names of the two towns from which our next assignment will be drawn.

ISABEL. So that you always know where you are going next?

SUPERVISOR. That's just it. I know and I don't know.
I know that it will be either Nice or Tours. But I
won't know which until the very week I leave. Can
you possibly appreciate the delicious torment of this
continual uncertainty?

ISABEL. So that every day of the three years you
have spent with us, your thoughts have been vibrating
between Nice—

SUPERVISOR. The beach, the casino, the boardwalk,
the sea—

ISABEL. And Tours?

SUPERVISOR. The castles, the churches, the plain and
the river. Now do you see what life can be? Tell me
frankly—between the riddle of life with me, and the
riddle of death—with him—which seems the more interesting?

ISABEL. I didn't know about this. It sounds marvellous. So that when you are in Nice—

SUPERVISOR. Or will it be Tours—?

ISABEL. You will have three whole years in which
to wonder about the next possibility?

SUPERVISOR. Chartres and Grenoble.

ISABEL. The valley and the mountain—

SUPERVISOR. Yes. And so by a series of pendulum
swings involving every earthly possibility—we come
at last to— *(Rises; steps Right.)*

ISABEL. Paris.

SUPERVISOR. Yes.

ISABEL. *(Rises)* What a beautiful cruise your life
must be! One can see its wake in your eyes!

SUPERVISOR. People talk of sailors' eyes. It's because when they pay their taxes, they never look into
the eyes of the collector. *(Crosses to Center)* It's because when they pass the customs, they never look at
the eyes of the official. It's because in a courtroom,
it never occurs to a litigant to take the judge's head
in his hands, and turn it gently to the light and gaze

into his pupils. In the eyes of a government official, believe me, they would see the reflection of an ocean no sailor ever saw. It is the ocean of life, Miss Isabel.

ISABEL. It's true. It's strange. I see it now in yours. It is blue.

SUPERVISOR. And do you like it, Miss Isabel?

ISABEL. I think— I like it very much.

SUPERVISOR. Ah! In that case—

(He goes to the door Right with a decisive air. The military BAND finishes its waltz. There is silence.)

ISABEL. What are you doing?

SUPERVISOR. Bolting the doors. *(Does so)* Locking the windows. *(Does so)* So. The room is now sealed off from the universe. I serve formal notice upon all intruders to keep out. *(Crosses above sofa)* Sit down, Miss Isabel. *(ISABEL sits on sofa.)* We have only to wait quietly a few minutes, and we shall be safe.

ISABEL. Oh, but—

SUPERVISOR. But be careful, Miss Isabel. No regrets. *(Looks toward door)* No reservations. In all likelihood, he is listening. The slightest word may be construed as an invitation.

ISABEL. My poor ghost!

(Offstage is heard a distant fanfare of TRUMPETS. The bolted door flies open. The GHOST appears. He is paler and more transparent than before, and rather more appealing.)

GHOST. *(Entering)* I may come in?

(ISABEL rises.)

SUPERVISOR. *(Crossing to Left Center)* You may not come in. The door is locked and bolted.

GHOST. *(To below table)* I have the key to the

enigma, Isabel! I can tell you everything, Isabel.
Isabel—ask this man to leave us.

SUPERVISOR. I regret. That is out of the question.

GHOST. I am speaking to Isabel.

SUPERVISOR. You will notice that Isabel is not speaking to you.

GHOST. Do you fancy that you are protecting her?
(The SUPERVISOR *bows.)* From what?

SUPERVISOR. I don't know. Therefore I must be doubly careful.

GHOST. Don't be afraid. I am not in the least dangerous.

SUPERVISOR. Perhaps not. But what you represent is dangerous.

GHOST. You mean—Death?

SUPERVISOR. It's your word.

GHOST. You think you can save her from that?

SUPERVISOR. I am quite sure.

GHOST. And suppose I am not alone? Suppose that Death is here with me? Suppose that Isabel sees something that you do not see?

SUPERVISOR. A girl sees all sorts of things that her husband doesn't see. It makes no difference—so long as he's there. *(Crosses to* ISABEL.*)*

GHOST. Oh. So you are married, Isabel?

SUPERVISOR. Not yet.

GHOST. You are engaged?

SUPERVISOR. The word is a little strong. I have asked Isabel to be my wife and she has not refused. I don't know exactly what you call this relationship—

GHOST. I call it vague.

SUPERVISOR. *(Crossing to Center)* Then obviously I cannot leave her with you for a moment.

GHOST. And suppose I leave, and come back when you're gone?

SUPERVISOR. You won't. You haven't the stamina. You haven't the time. The fact is, you too seem a little vague, my friend,—you are fading. You grow more transparent by the moment. If I were you, I'd make a good exit while I still had the wherewithal.

GHOST. Isabel—

SUPERVISOR. If you can pass only through closed doors, *(Indicating door)* I'll be glad to close this one for you.

GHOST. Isabel—

ISABEL. *(Crossing to* SUPERVISOR*)* Dear Supervisor—tomorrow I will listen to you, I promise. But let me have this moment—this last little moment—with him. *(Crosses to* GHOST.*)*

SUPERVISOR. If I should desert you in the face of my enemy, tomorrow you would despise me. *(Steps down.)*

ISABEL. *(Turns to* SUPERVISOR*)* But he has come to give me the answer to the riddle that has troubled me all my life!

SUPERVISOR. I'm not in favor of the answers to riddles. A riddle is amusing only while it is a riddle. An answered riddle has no dignity whatever—it becomes an absurdity. What riddle?

ISABEL. The riddle of death.

SUPERVISOR. The death of a star, of an ideal, of a flower?

ISABEL. The death of a man.

SUPERVISOR. *(Crossing to Left Center)* That's not even a riddle. Do these trifles interest you? Everyone in the Weights and Measures knows the answer to that. Death is the next step after the pension—it's perpetual retirement without pay. And even if that were a riddle—which it isn't—what makes you think the dead would know the answer? *(Steps in)* If the dead know any more about death than the living know about life, I congratulate them on their insight. And that's all I have to say. *(Turns Left.)*

ISABEL. Well, if you won't go, let him speak in your presence. Perhaps he will?

GHOST. He will not. *(Breaks Right, below table.)*

ISABEL. You could stop your ears a moment.

SUPERVISOR. I'm sorry, but that is just what I can't do. I am provided with eyelids. But not with earlids.

GHOST. Such is the lump of concrete out of which destiny is forced to make spirits!

SUPERVISOR. *(Crossing to* GHOST*)* Don't worry about me, my friend. If there's one thing I'm sure of, it's that when my turn comes I will make a perfectly adequate spirit.

GHOST. Oh, you think so?

SUPERVISOR. When I come to my final assignment, my colleagues will know that I was always dependable as a man and that I can be relied upon as a ghost. They will know that I lived my life fully to the extent of my capacity—that I never flagged in my duty to those I served nor in my devotion to those I loved. *(To* ISABEL*)* They will know that in the years I spent in Isabel's town, I never let a day pass without assuring myself that Isabel was well and happy. *(Crosses to* ISABEL*)* They may remember the hour I spent one night scratching out with my penknife the word that someone had painted on her door, the morning when I replaced the broken milk bottles on her doorstep, the afternoon when I saved her mail from being soaked by the rain. They will realize that in my modest way, I did my best always to soften the blows that fortune aimed at her. *(To Center.)*

ISABEL. *(Her hand out)* Dear Robert—!

GHOST. I beg pardon?

ISABEL. Nothing.

GHOST. Why do you say, "Dear Robert"?

ISABEL. Because—. Why? Do you mind my saying it?

GHOST. *(Crossing to Left of chair Left of table)* Not at all. I thank you for saying it. It shows me where I stand with relation to dear Robert. Thanks very much. You have saved me from committing a great folly, the greatest possible folly. I was about to betray an inviolable secret for the sake of a girl. Luckily she betrayed me first.

ISABEL. But how have I betrayed you?

GHOST. And that's how it always is and how it always will be. And there you have the whole story of young girls.

SUPERVISOR. Now what is he talking about?

GHOST. I am speaking of young girls. Sitting in the park, staring at the passerby without looking at him; lounging with their bicycles at a railroad crossing, in order to welcome the traveler with a gesture of parting; seated at their windows with a book in the lamplight, a pool of radiance between shadow and shadow; like flowers in summer, in winter like thoughts of flowers; they dispose themselves so gracefully in the world of men that we are convinced we see in them not the childhood of humanity, but its supreme expression. Between the world of a young girl and the world of the spirit, the wall seems no more than a gossamer; one would say that at any moment, through the soul of a girl, the infinite could flow into the finite and possess it utterly. But all at once—

SUPERVISOR. Now, please—! *(A step down.)*

GHOST. The man appears. They watch him intently. He has found some tricks with which to enhance his worth in their eyes. He stands on his hind legs in order to shed the rain better and to hang medals on his chest. He swells his biceps. They quail before him with hypocritical admiration, trembling with such fear as not even a tiger inspires, not realizing that of all the carnivorous animals, this biped alone has ineffective teeth. And as they gaze at him, the windows of the soul, through which once they saw the myriad colors of the outer world, cloud over, grow opaque, and in that moment, the story is over. *(Steps up.)*

SUPERVISOR. *(Steps in)* And life begins—

GHOST. Yes. The pleasure of the bed begins. And the pleasure of the table. And the habit of pleasure. And the pleasure of jealousy—and the pleasure of cruelty.

SUPERVISOR. *(A step to* ISABEL*)* It's a lie. Don't listen to him, Isabel.

GHOST. And the pleasure of suffering. And last of all, the pleasure of indifference. So, little by little the pearl loses its lustre and long before it dies, it is dead.

ISABEL. Oh, Ghost—Ghost—! If this is what life is, save me from it!

GHOST. No, Isabel. Your Supervisor is right. You belong not to us, but to him. You are as false and as shallow as the others. What you really love is not the truth, but the pleasure of vibrating endlessly between two falsehoods, between Nice and Tours. Well, you are welcome to your little game. It is not through you that the riddle will be solved and the miracle accomplished.

ISABEL. Oh please—tell me.

GHOST. I will tell you nothing. *(Crosses to below table)* I will tell you not even the name of the little flower which carpets the fields of death, whose petals I shall bring one day to someone more fortunate than you. Take her in your arms, now, Supervisor. Spring that wolf-trap of yours about her—and may she never again escape while she lives!

ISABEL. Oh please—please!

(She runs into the arms of the GHOST, *who kisses her tenderly, then pushes her away.)*

GHOST. Farewell, Isabel. *(He backs out Right.)*

*(*ISABEL *stands still a moment, then she swoons. The* SUPERVISOR *runs to her, catches her and carries her to the sofa.)*

SUPERVISOR. *(Up Center)* Doctor! Doctor! Help! Quickly! *(Crosses to below sofa, kneels.)*

(But it is the INSPECTOR *who runs in Left.)*

INSPECTOR. *(Above sofa)* What's happened? Has he come? Has he gone?

SUPERVISOR. He tried to take her with him. But she's still breathing—.

INSPECTOR. *(Feeling her forehead)* Her head is hot.

SUPERVISOR. Her feet are cold.

INSPECTOR. He must have tried to drag her off by the feet. Rather clumsy of him.

ISABEL. *(Opening her eyes)* Where am I?

SUPERVISOR. In my arms, darling. *(She faints again.)* Oh! She's gone again!

INSPECTOR. Because your answer was insufficient. She is trying to come back from very far away. She requires precise directions.

ISABEL. *(Stirring restlessly)* Where am I? Where am I?

INSPECTOR. On the planet Earth, my child, the third satellite of the sun. And if you feel a little dizzy, it's only because this earth is spinning. One soon gets used to it.

ISABEL. Who am I?

SUPERVISOR. Isabel. Isabel.

INSPECTOR. You are one of the higher mammals. Species: human. Sex: female. And a first-rate specimen.

ISABEL. *(Listening)* What's that?

SUPERVISOR. It's the military band rehearsing.

INSPECTOR. It's a wave motion of the air, little female, vibrating on your eardrums, which convey the impulse through the hammer, the anvil and the stirrup to the cochlea of the ear. There—she's coming to. You see? Nothing like a dose of science to restore one to one's senses. Give a young schoolteacher a whiff of a technical term, and she pricks up her ears at once.

SUPERVISOR. Her heart has stopped! *(Crosses Right, above table)* Help! Help! Doctor!

(The DOCTOR *comes in Right, unhurried, crosses to* ISABEL. *He is followed by a curious parcel of citi-*

zens, including MR. ADRIAN *and* PAPA TELLIER *to above table.)*

DOCTOR. Here I am. It's all right. I've brought the remedy.

SUPERVISOR. *(Crossing Left)* Doctor! She's dead!

DOCTOR. Don't worry.

MR. ADRIAN. I smell something. What is that? Brimstone.

DOCTOR. You're just in time. Mr. Adrian. Sit at that table, please.

PAPA TELLIER. Open the windows. The windows. She needs air.

DOCTOR. *(Crossing to table)* She doesn't need air. (SUPERVISOR *crosses to below sofa.)* She's not breathing. Sit down. Here's a deck of cards. When I give the word, begin to play.

(TELLIER *sits below table;* ADRIAN *Right of it.)*

PAPA TELLIER. To play what?

DOCTOR. Anything. Casino.

[*(The* GIRLS *crowd in Left and form a line above sofa.)*

THE GIRLS. Is she alive? Is she alive?

DOCTOR. Not yet.

INSPECTOR. *(To Center)* Clear out, children.

DOCTOR. No, no. Come in. Come in, all of you. We shall all have to work at this. Now. When I give the word, you will start reciting your lessons.

GIRLS. Which lessons?

DOCTOR. Any lessons.

INSPECTOR. Doctor, what in the name of heaven—?

(ARMANDE *enters Right, head in door;* LEONIDE *behind her.)*

ARMANDE. I hear she is burnt to a cinder.

SUPERVISOR. Not quite.

ARMANDE. The best thing is to rub her nose with garlic.

DOCTOR. Never mind the garlic. Come in, please. And your sister. (ARMANDE *enters to above chair Right.*) And start chattering.

LEONIDE. *(Comes in, to down Right)* What does he say?

ARMANDE. To start chattering.

LEONIDE. Why should we chatter? We never chatter. Who says we chatter?

DOCTOR. That's it. Don't stop.

INSPECTOR. *(To Right end of sofa)* Doctor, what is all this nonsense?

DOCTOR. Don't you understand? Isabel is neither drowned nor run over. Her body is in perfect condition. But her spirit has left it. To induce it to return, we must batter at the gate of death with the sounds of life.

(MAYOR *enters to down Left.*)

INSPECTOR. Wouldn't it be better if you gave her some adrenalin?

DOCTOR. *(Crossing up Right Center)* What she needs is not adrenalin, but persuasion.

INSPECTOR. I don't understand.

MAYOR. Nor I.

MR. ADRIAN. Do you get it?

PAPA TELLIER. What?

LEONIDE. What are they saying?

ARMANDE. That they don't understand.

LEONIDE. Who does?

THE GIRLS. We do! We do!

(DOCTOR *comes Center.*)

MAYOR. You do?

VIOLA. We have to make life more real than death for her.

LUCY. We have to bring the sounds of life to bear on her spirit.

GILBERTE. Like a ray of sunshine.

DAISY. Like a symphony.

LUCY. Like artificial respiration.

IRENE. And when she feels the tempo of living—

DAISY. When she catches the rhythm—

VIOLA. A word will touch her heart—

GILBERTE. And her heart will begin to beat.

DOCTOR. Bravo, children! And now that you understand, Mr. Mayor, will you take charge of the street noises? *(Goes up and opens windows.)*

MAYOR. The blacksmith? The carpenter?

DOCTOR. *(Crossing down Center)* The carts. The trucks. *(The* MAYOR *hurries out Right.)* Inspector, you will contribute at regular intervals the phrases of your profession.

INSPECTOR. I have no professional phrases other than those that best express the principles of Truth and Justice.

DOCTOR. That's it exactly. *(To the* SUPERVISOR*)* And you—

SUPERVISOR. I love you, Isabel!

DOCTOR. That's it.

INSPECTOR. As an elected official of a glorious democracy—

SUPERVISOR. I love you.

DOCTOR. *(Taps with his stick)* The "I love you" is a trifle weak, the "Glorious Democracy," a bit too loud. And please remember this is a very difficult transition to manage. We must keep in time. Ready?

(He taps the table with his stick, like the conductor of an orchestra. After a preliminary flourish, he gives the signal to begin, and the symphony begins, loud, soft, legato or staccato, according to his beat. The cardplayers begin playing, the

WOMEN *begin chattering, the* INSPECTOR *begins a speech. From the open window, come the SOUNDS of life—not an imitation, but life itself—an auto horn, a motor racing, a carpenter hammering, the ring of a hammer on an anvil, steps, laughter, a passerby whistling "Parlez-moi d'amour.")*

THE GIRLS. Two times two is four.
ADRIAN. Your deal.
THE GIRLS. Two times three is six.
TELLIER. Cut.
THE GIRLS. Two times four is eight.
INSPECTOR. Imperishable honor—
THE GIRLS. Two times five is ten.
ARMANDE. I don't like to send it to the cleaner.
THE GIRLS. Henry the Fourth died in 1610.
INSPECTOR. Socio-economic determinism.
TELLIER. I'll take the Jack.
THE GIRLS. Louis the Thirteenth—
LEONIDE. The yolk of two eggs.
INSPECTOR. Ensuring a living wage for all.
THE GIRLS. Mounted the throne—
SUPERVISOR. I love you, Isabel.
THE GIRLS. Louis the Fourteenth was born—
LEONIDE. In a moderate even, not too hot—
SUPERVISOR. I love you, Isabel.
INSPECTOR. The Progressive Party—
THE GIRLS. Ascended the throne—
LEONIDE. Larded with suet.
TELLIER. And the ace of spades for me.
THE GIRLS. Died in the year 1715.

(The DOCTOR *is in his stride now. He signals for a pianissimo passage. The military band, offstage, accompanies throughout.)*

INSPECTOR. The re-orientation of basic products—
SUPERVISOR. I love you, Isabel.

INSPECTOR. The implementation of government policy—

ARMANDE. A buttonhole stitch is the only solution.

TELLIER. Take some and leave some. I'll take the ten.

INSPECTOR. Special areas of legislation.

THE GIRLS. 1793—The Terror.

INSPECTOR. Liquidation of the lower brackets.

ADRIAN. Building sixes, if you please.

THE GIRLS. Louis the Sixteenth lost his head—

SUPERVISOR. I love you, Isabel.

ARMANDE. Chiffon velvet doesn't wear—

TELLIER. Two of clubs.

(And now crescendo and marcato.)

THE GIRLS. Columbus discovered—

INSPECTOR. The business cycle—

THE GIRLS. In Fourteen hundred and ninety-two.

LEONIDE. With a woman he found in the gutter—

INSPECTOR. Horizontal integration.

THE GIRLS. Magellan sailed around the world—

INSPECTOR. Cartelization of industry.

THE GIRLS. Fifteen hundred and twenty-one.

ARMANDE. She wore black lace petticoats.

LEONIDE. Black lace? Really?

ISABEL. *(Shuddering)* Black lace! Really!

ALL. What? What did she say?

SUPERVISOR. Doctor! She spoke!

DOCTOR. *(Crossing to Center)* If black lace petticoats won't do the trick, nothing will. We're getting through to her. Now once more—and all together—

(ALL crowd in.)

THE GIRLS. Vasco da Gama—

LEONIDE. Brown on both sides.

ADRIAN. I have cards—

INSPECTOR. And vested interests—

THE GIRLS. Sailed to India—

TELLIER. Spades as well—
THE GIRLS. In fourteen hundred ninety-eight—
ARMANDE. Lined throughout with crimson satin—
ISABEL. *(Murmurs restlessly)* Crimson—crimson satin—
INSPECTOR. Poor girl—
SUPERVISOR. Isabel—
ISABEL. *(Sitting up suddenly)* Robert!
SUPERVISOR. I love you!

(And she is in his arms.)

INSPECTOR. She's saved.
THE GIRLS. She's saved! She's saved!
ISABEL. Black lace! Crimson satin! Oh Robert!— life is so beautiful!
DOCTOR. She's lost. *(Crosses Right, below table.)*
LEONIDE. What? What are they saying?
ARMANDE. She's saved and lost. *(WARN Curtain.)*
LEONIDE. What a scatterbrain!
INSPECTOR. *(Taking the floor)* Fellow citizens, the Administration desires to thank you for your cooperation in this most unusual and difficult case. Trivial as it may now seem, it was nevertheless pregnant—
LEONIDE. What's he saying?
ARMANDE. Pregnant.
LEONIDE. What? Already?

(ISABEL and SUPERVISOR rise.)

INSPECTOR. With incalculable consequences. I am happy to say that through the combined efforts of government and science, we have brought to a successful conclusion—
THE GIRLS. Conclusion.
INSPECTOR. One of the most dangerous outbreaks of radical activity in the history of the Republic.
THE GIRLS. Republic.
INSPECTOR. Quiet, you. After this victory, we may

be sure that the natural order will resume its normal functioning in accordance with logic and common sense—

MAYOR. *(The* MAYOR *runs on Right, breathlessly, goes to* INSPECTOR) Inspector! Inspector! The lottery!

INSPECTOR. What's wrong with the lottery?

MAYOR. Guess who won the motorcycle?

INSPECTOR. Who?

MAYOR. The Mother Superior.

INSPECTOR. Aha! And the grand cash prize?

THE GIRLS. Monsieur Dumas! Monsieur Dumas!

MAYOR. Monsieur Dumas, the millionaire!

INSPECTOR. Mr. Mayor, my congratulations. Enlightened democracy is working as usual. I restore your district to you in perfect order. The danger is past—

MAYOR. And Isabel?

INSPECTOR. Isabel is saved.

ISABEL. I love you, Robert.

DOCTOR. The interlude is over.

(The military BAND crashes into a march.)

CURTAIN

THE ENCHANTED

PROPERTY PLOT

ACT ONE

Flowers
Shrubbery
Hearing aid
Blueboard
Pocket glass

ACT TWO

Flashlights
Letters
Corkscrews
Cigarettes
Five francs
Toothpick
Fountain pen
Cough drops
Rubber band
Comb
Money
Key
Pistols
Pitchpipes
Tuning

ACT THREE

Document
Playing Cards

THE ENCHANTED
MUSIC CUE SHEET
ACT ONE

Line Cues	*Cue #*	*Music*
	1-a-on	Overture CURTAIN rises after 3 individual notes Play to end of cut
	1-b off	
(MAYOR enters) VOICES (offstage): "Hello, hello, hello—"	2-a on	Covering entrance of ISABEL and little girls
MAYOR: "Oh, Miss Isabel, what a start you gave us!"	2-b fade under	
ISABEL: "The Spring is our classroom, Doctor."	2-c off	
INSPECTOR (offstage): "You demand proofs."	3-a on	INSPECTOR enters with music Play to end of cut
	3-b off	

(INSPECTOR continues)

INSPECTOR: "But not spirits of man."	4-a on	(DOCTOR: "That's not so clear— spoken over music MANGEBOIS sisters enter. Play to end of cut
	4-b off	
(MAYOR speaks) ARMANDE: "Good afternoon, gentlemen."	5-a on	MANGEBOIS exit ISABEL and little girls enter
MARIE-LOUISE: "Who's that funny man?"	5-b—quick fade and off	
INSPECTOR: —"put a hedge-hog"	6-a on	
INSPECTOR: "Arthur! Arthur!"	6-b—quick fade and off	
DOCTOR: "And now my assistants"	7-a on—low	
DOCTOR: "the crickets"	7-b—fade and off	
DOCTOR: "The overture begins"	8-a on	Play to end of cut
	8-b—fade and off	
ISABEL: "The trumpets of the garrison."	9-a on	Play to end of cut
	9-b off	
DOCTOR: "shadows of cypress and pine—"	10-a on— low	

Doctor: "You see, it's done."	10-b—swell to full	Ghost appears
	10-c off	When Isabel sees him—
Isabel: "We're quite alone." (Ghost exits)	11-a on— low	Covering rest of Isabel's speech— lines interspersed with music
Curtain—simultaneously with	11-b off	

ACT TWO

	12-a on	Overture Play to end of cut
	12-b off	Curtain Follows 12-B immediately (Phrase introducing little girls' song)
	13-a on	
	13-b off	
Supervisor: "Besides, it's time for recess. Vanish!"	13-c on	Girls exit
	13-d off	
	14-a on	Inspector and Mayor enter
Doctor: "The other world, perhaps—"	14-b off	Play to end of cut

INSPECTOR (Enters) "All right, gentlemen."	15-a on	EXECUTIONERS enter, play to end of cut
	15-b off	
INSPECTOR: "Very well, then. Run along."	15-c on	EXECUTIONERS exit, to couple of bars of cut
	15-d off	
DOCTOR: "As safe in a whirlwind as in a church." (Puts pipe to his lips)	16-a on	
	16-b off	Play to end of cut DOCTOR exits, is off on last note
	17-a on	Follows 16-b after a couple of beats
	17-b—fade and off	ISABEL enters to music, sits
	18-a on	Follows 17-b immediately
GHOST: "Did I keep you waiting?"	18-b—fade slowly and off	
DOCTOR: "I apologize because—"	19-a—a fade in—soft	Covers DOCTOR's speech

DOCTOR: "and the spectre is false."

19-b off

20-a on | Follows 19-b immediately GHOST rises.

INSPECTOR: "seems to be something wrong with my eyes."

20-b—fade and off | Under INSPECTOR'S speech

GHOST: "with the others, Isabel, with all the others." 21-a on

GIRLS dance around; quick Curtain on last note

21-b off

ACT THREE

22-a on | Curtain rises halfway through cut
Stage empty for 5 secs.

INSPECTOR, MAYOR and GIRLS enter 22-b off | Play to end of cut
GIRLS: "Sentence."
INSPECTOR: "Not yet!" 23-a on | Play through to—

INSPECTOR: "paragraph 8, section 2. In witness whereof—" 23-b off, sharp

ISABEL: "Please stay. Please."		
DOCTOR: "As you wish."	24-a on	Play to end of cut
	24-b off	
SUPERVISOR: "The slightest word may be construed as an invitation."	25-a on	Play to end of cut
	25-b off	
GHOST: "Farewell, Isabel."	25-c on	Play to end of cut
	25-d off	
INSPECTOR: "You are one of the higher mammals. Species: human—"	26-a on, low	
SUPERVISOR: "military band rehearsing."	26-b off	
DOCTOR: "We must keep in time. Ready?" (He signals)	26-c on	
ISABEL: "Black lace, really?"	26-d off, quick	
DOCTOR: "Once more, and all together."	26-e on	
ARMANDE: "lined throughout with crimson satin—" (ISABEL moves)	26-f off, quick	As ISABEL moves
ISABEL: "I love you, Robert."		
SUPERVISOR: "Isabel."	27-a on, low	
DOCTOR: "The interlude is over."	27-b on, full	
		Play as Curtain comes down
	27-c off	As Curtain touches floor

THE ENCHANTED

MUSIC RECORDS

ACT ONE

Side # 1
Cue # 1.
      2., 6.
      3., 14. (Act Two)
      4.
      5.
      7.
      8.

Side # 2
Cue # 9.
      10., 18. (Act Two)
      11.

ACT TWO

      12.
      13.
      15.
      16.

Side # 3
      17., 19.
      20.
      21.

ACT THREE

      22.
Side # 4
      23., 26.
      24.
      25.
      27.

We can supply this music on two 12″ records at
$3.50 each, postpaid. The royalty for the use of same
is $5.00 per performance.

BACK DROP

2 GROUND ROWS

TREES

TREES

TREES

TREES

HOLLOW LOG

TREE STUMP

PORTAL

PORTAL

SCENE DESIGN—ACTS I-II
"THE ENCHANTED"

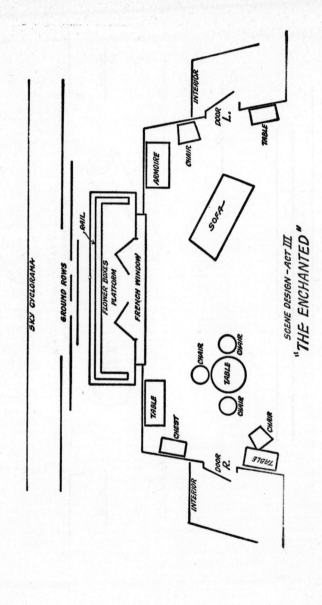

SCENE DESIGN — ACT III
"THE ENCHANTED"

X MARKS THE SPOT

Mystery comedy. 3 acts. By George Van Edgar. 6 males, 6 females. Interior. Modern costumes.

The action all takes place within a few hours one night in Madame Berteaux's Wax Museum, located on Pastime Island, a pleasure resort. Madame Berteaux is preparing a new wax exhibit, depicting the famous Doloman Murder Case. Three years previously, Charlotte Doloman had been slain with an axe, and her nephew, Boyd Doloman, sentenced to life imprisonment for the crime. Now Madame and her charming niece, Nila, have obtained the original furnishings of the death room so that they can show, as part of the exhibit, the actual scene of the crime! And they have enlisted Arthur Doloman, Boyd's brother, to help them arrange the exhibit authentically. But—on this very night, Boyd escapes from the state penitentiary and is believed to be heading for Pastime Island! From this point, riot runs loose. When the escaped murderer tangles with the Berteauxs, with Ophelia Coots, their shivery seamstress, and with Achilles, the Strong Man, Serpentina, the Snake Charmer, and La Barbe, the Bearded Lady, from the freak show next door, everything happens—including a couple of murders, shots and screams in the dark and a poisonous cobra at large in the wax museum!

(Budget Play.) Price, 75 cents.

A GIRL NAMED PAT!

Farce-comedy. 3 acts. By Kit Mearson. 4 males, 7 females. Interior. Modern costumes.

When wealthy young heiress, Patricia Gordon, wanders into the lobby of "Crash Inn," a summer resort hotel, she inadvertently finds herself in the middle of a baffling sequence of events. For reasons of her own, Pat has registered at the inn under the assumed name of Mary Jones. Shortly after her arrival, Pat is startled to hear that a crime has taken place in the neighborhood. The Police are hot on the trail of "a girl named Pat." Of course, Pat isn't aware of the fact that there is a boy at the inn named Pat Dodd and that he is eloping with a close friend of hers, one Juliet Condon. There is also a married couple present named Mr. and Mrs. Patt. In the mixup that results from her presence at the inn, Pat is forced to use all of her ingenuity to remain out of the clutches of the law.

(Budget Play.) Price, 75 cents.

WITNESS FOR THE PROSECUTION

Melodrama. 3 acts. By Agatha Christie. 17 men, 5 women. Interior. Modern costumes.

Winner of New York Critics Circle Award and the Antoinette Perry Award. One of the greatest mystery melodramas in years. The story is that of a likable young drifter who is suspected of bashing in the head of a middle-aged, wealthy spinster who has willed her tidy estate to him. His only alibi is the word of his wife, a queer customer, indeed, who, in the dock, repudiates the alibi and charges him with the murder. Then a mystery woman appears with damaging letters against the wife and the young man is freed. We learn, however, that the mystery woman is actually the wife, who has perjured herself because she felt direct testimony for her husband would not have freed him. But when the young man turns his back on his wife for another woman, we realize he really was the murderer. Then Miss Christie gives us a triple-flip ending that leaves the audience gasping, while serving up justice to the young man. (Royalty, $50.00 where available.) Price, $1.00.

THE MOUSETRAP

The longest-run straight play in London history.

Melodrama. 3 acts. By Agatha Christie. 5 men, 3 women. Interior.

The author of *Ten Little Indians* and *Witness for the Prosecution* comes forth with another English hit. About a group of strangers stranded in a boarding house during a snow storm, one of whom is a murderer. The suspects include the newly married couple who run the house, a spinster, an architect, a retired Army major, a strange little man who claims his car overturned in a drift, and a feminine jurist. Into their midst comes a policeman, traveling on skiis. He no sooner arrives than the jurist is killed. To get to the rationale of the murderer's pattern, the policeman probes the background of everyone present, and rattles a lot of skeletons. But in another famous Agatha Christie switch finish, it is the policeman—or, rather the man disguised as a policeman—who shoulders the blame. Chalk up another superb intrigue for the foremost mystery writer of her half century.

(Royalty, $50.00.) Price, $1.25.

A Book of Anagrams –
An Ancient Word Game

Daniel H. Wieczorek

A Book of Anagrams – An Ancient Word Game

ISBN: 1468180878
ISBN-13: 978-1468180879

DEDICATION

Dedicated to my Mother – who always encouraged me to have an interest in words, vocabulary, dictionaries and reading and always made sure that, of the limited budget available, some part of it was to be used for books. Thanks Mom.

Also dedicated to the Sisters, Servants of the Immaculate Heart of Mary, who taught me at Saints Peter and Paul School when I was a youngster – their dedication to teaching to the highest standards also encouraged me to take a very deep interest in reading, vocabulary and words. Their continual insistence of, "go to the dictionary", when we did not know the meaning of a new word surely gave me a deep respect for vocabulary and dictionaries.

Other books by Daniel H. Wieczorek include:

Outdoor Photography of Japan: Through the Seasons
(co-authored with Kazuya Numazawa)
(Print and E-book Editions)

Some Violets of Eastern Japan
(co-authored with Kazuya Numazawa)
(Print and E-book Editions)

English – Ilokano And Ilokano – English Dictionary
(Print and E-book Editions)

These titles are all available through your local bookseller (search the internet for the appropriate ISBN's) or through Amazon.

FOREWORD

What is an anagram? An anagram is a rearrangement of the letters of one word or phrase to form another word or phrase. In this work you will find fifty 9-letter words which have been disassembled and the letters placed in a grid. It's your job to find as many words as you can in the scrambled 9 letters and in so doing, also find the original 9-letter word.

A web search for the history of anagrams will give you many more results than you want to read. Let it suffice to say that they have been around for a LONG TIME! It seems that they've been around since at least the 3rd century BC and the Greek poet Lycophron. It also seems that anagrams were believed to have mystical or prophetic meaning in some eras of history. In the Middle Ages, anagrammatists often entertained, by creating witty anagrams of people's names.

For the anagrams which are listed in this work, the Anagrams tool of the CD-ROM version of the 3rd Edition of the American Heritage Dictionary was used. Several results for each word were then deleted – for example abbreviations such as ROM, RAM, UNESCO, DOS, CPU, ECT, EEG and so on. Capitalized words which were repeats of lowercase words were usually deleted – for example Red, Trine, Host, Sir and so on. It was felt that a single entry (lowercase) was enough. Please forgive me if you find more words – the edition of the American Heritage Dictionary which was used was created in 1993, it is an older version and may not have the newest words. You may occasionally find an abbreviation which I failed to delete, they were not intentionally left here, but were discovered by reviewers.

Also, please forgive the use of different size fonts on the various results pages. It was desired to fit the results for each word on a single page and therefore a font size was used which permitted this.

The base word (the real word) from which each anagram was created is underlined on each results page. In some cases, when it is felt the reader may not know the word, the definition of the base word has been included on the results page.

By the way, while you work, for example, on Anagram #2 you will be able to see the results list from Anagram #1, so it is suggested that you use your hand or a piece of paper to cover that result list while you work on the following anagram so as to not give yourself hints and clues. There were two alternatives available for showing the results pages – either immediately after each anagram, or all of the results pages at the end of the book. It seemed that the alternative selected was the best way to go.

TABLE OF CONTENTS

#1

How many words can you make from these 9 letters? Every word must contain the letter "E". You can use only these 9 letters and a letter cannot be used more than once in any word. It's possible to make one 9-letter word.

Score: 20 words or more – EXCELLENT
    15 words or more – VERY GOOD
    10 words or more - GOOD

Hint: don't forget the plural forms of words, for example toe is 1 word and toes is a 2nd word. It's possible to make 116 words of 2 or more letters. (See following page for answers).

Answers:

1

1. ego	41. hose	81. shone
2. egoism	42. ingest	82. signet
3. egos	43. inset	83. sine
4. egotism	44. item	84. singe
5. eight	45. items	85. site
6. emit	46. me	86. smite
7. emits	47. men	87. smote
8. emoting	48. mesh	88. some
9. eon	49. meshing	89. something
10. eosin	50. met	90. stein
11. ethos	51. mien	91. stem
12. gem	52. mines	92. steno
13. gems	53. mite	93. stone
14. gent	54. mites	94. ten
15. gents	55. moisten	95. tens
16. get	56. monies	96. the
17. gets	57. mote	97. theism
18. gnome	58. motes	98. them
19. gnomes	59. neigh	99. then
20. goes	60. neighs	100. thine
21. gone	61. nest	101. those
22. he	62. net	102. tie
23. heist	63. nets	103. ties
24. hem	64. noes	104. time
25. hems	65. noise	105. times
26. hen	66. nose	106. tine
27. hens	67. note	107. tines
28. hinge	68. notes	108. tinge
29. hinges	69. omen	109. tinges
30. hoe	70. omens	110. toe
31. hoeing	71. one	111. toeing
32. hoes	72. ones	112. toes
33. hogtie	73. onset	113. tome
34. hogties	74. semi	114. tomes
35. home	75. sent	115. tone
36. homes	76. set	116. tones
37. homiest	77. she	
38. hone	78. shine	This page
39. hones	79. shoe	Photocopiable
40. honest	80. shoeing	

#2

How many words can you make from these 9 letters? Every word must contain the letter "A". You can use only these 9 letters and a letter cannot be used more than once in any word (you may use 2 S's). It's possible to make one 9-letter word.

Score: 20 words or more – EXCELLENT

    15 words or more – VERY GOOD

    10 words or more - GOOD

Hint: don't forget the plural forms of words, for example mat is 1 word and mats is a 2nd word. It's possible to make 123 words of 3 or more letters. (See following page for answers).

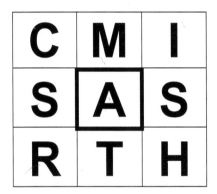

Answers: ___

3

1. act	43. cram	85. rat
2. acts	44. crams	86. rats
3. aim	45. crash	87. sac
4. aims	46. crass	88. sacs
5. air	47. hair	89. sari
6. airs	48. hairs	90. saris
7. Amish	49. ham	91. sash
8. amiss	50. hams	92. sat
9. arc	51. harm	93. scam
10. arch	52. harms	94. scams
11. arcs	53. hart	95. scar
12. arm	54. harts	96. scars
13. arms	55. has	97. scat
14. art	56. hast	98. scats
15. arts	57. hat	99. scram
16. ash	58. hats	100. scrams
17. ass	59. mach	101. sham
18. astir	60. mar	102. shams
19. cam	61. march	103. sitar
20. cams	62. mars	104. sitars
21. car	63. marsh	105. smart
22. cars	64. mart	106. smarts
23. cart	65. marts	107. smash
24. carts	66. mash	108. stair
25. cash	67. mass	109. stairs
26. cast	68. mast	110. star
27. casts	69. mastic	111. starch
28. cat	70. mastics	112. stars
29. cats	71. masts	113. stash
30. chair	72. mat	114. stria
31. chairs	73. match	115. tar
32. char	74. math	116. tars
33. charm	75. mats	117. tarsi
34. charms	76. mica	118. Thai
35. chars	77. Micah	119. Thais
36. chart	78. micas	120. tram
37. charts	79. miscast	121. trams
38. chasm	80. racism	122. trash
39. chasms	81. racist	123. tsar
40. chat	82. ram	
41. chats	83. rams	
42. Christmas	84. rash	

4

#3

How many words can you make from these 9 letters? Every word must contain the letter "E". You can use only these 9 letters and a letter cannot be used more than once in any word (you may use 2 E's). It's possible to make one 9-letter word.

Score: 20 words or more – EXCELLENT

    15 words or more – VERY GOOD

    10 words or more - GOOD

Hint: don't forget the plural forms of words, for example fee is 1 word and fees is a 2nd word. It's possible to make 108 words of 2 or more letters. (See following page for answers).

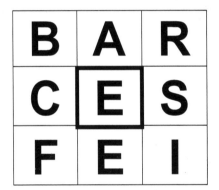

Answers:

_____ _____ _____ _____
_____ _____ _____ _____
_____ _____ _____ _____
_____ _____ _____ _____
_____ _____ _____ _____
_____ _____ _____ _____
_____ _____ _____ _____
_____ _____ _____ _____
_____ _____ _____ _____
_____ _____ _____ _____
_____ _____ _____ _____

1. ace
2. acerb
3. aces
4. acre
5. acres
6. aerie
7. aeries
8. afire
9. are
10. Aries
11. arise
12. ascribe
13. bare
14. bares
15. base
16. baser
17. be
18. bear
19. bears
20. bee
21. beef
22. beefs
23. beer
24. beers
25. bees
26. bier
27. biers
28. brace
29. braces
30. braise
31. brief
32. briefcase
33. briefs
34. cafe
35. cafes
36. care
37. cares
38. caries
39. case
40. cease
41. Ceres
42. cerise
43. crease
44. Cree
45. Crees
46. cries
47. ear
48. ears
49. ease
50. easier
51. era
52. erase
53. ere
54. face
55. faces
56. faerie
57. faeries
58. farce
59. farces
60. fare
61. fares
62. fear
63. fears
64. feces
65. fee
66. fees
67. fiber
68. fibers
69. fibre
70. fibres
71. fie
72. fierce
73. fire
74. firebase
75. fires
76. free
77. frees
78. fries
79. ice
80. ices
81. ire
82. rabies
83. race
84. races
85. raise
86. reef
87. reefs
88. rice
89. rices
90. rife
91. rise
92. saber
93. sabre
94. safe
95. safer
96. scare
97. scree
98. scribe
99. sea
100. sear
101. sec
102. see
103. seer
104. sera
105. sere
106. serf
107. serif
108. sire

#4

How many words can you make from these 9 letters? Every word must contain the letter "E". You can use only these 9 letters and a letter cannot be used more than once in any word. It's possible to make one 9-letter word.

Score: 20 words or more – EXCELLENT

    15 words or more – VERY GOOD

    10 words or more - GOOD

It's possible to make 135 words of 4 or more letters. (See following page for answers).

Answers:

1. agent	46. heating	91. niter
2. ahem	47. hegira	92. nitre
3. airmen	48. heir	93. rage
4. amen	49. hermit	94. ragtime
5. amine	50. hernia	95. raiment
6. anger	51. hinge	96. ramie
7. ante	52. hinter	97. range
8. anthem	53. hire	98. rate
9. anther	54. image	99. ream
10. argent	55. inert	100. reaming
11. earn	56. ingrate	101. regain
12. earth	57. inmate	102. reign
13. eating	58. inter	103. rein
14. eight	59. irate	104. remain
15. emir	60. item	105. remit
16. emit	61. magnet	106. rent
17. enigma	62. mane	107. retain
18. gainer	63. mange	108. retina
19. gaiter	64. manger	109. rhea
20. game	65. mare	110. rime
21. gamer	66. marine	111. rite
22. gamier	67. marten	112. tame
23. gamine	68. mate	113. tamer
24. garment	69. mean	114. tare
25. garnet	70. meant	115. team
26. gate	71. meat	116. teaming
27. gather	72. merit	117. tear
28. gear	73. meting	118. tearing
29. gent	74. mien	119. term
30. germ	75. migrate	120. terming
31. German	76. minaret	121. tern
32. granite	77. mine	122. thane
33. grate	78. minter	123. their
34. great	79. mirage	124. them
35. grime	80. mire	125. then
36. hanger	81. mite	126. thine
37. hare	82. miter	127. tier
38. harem	83. mitre	128. tiger
39. hate	84. name	129. time
40. hater	85. namer	130. timer
41. hear	86. near	131. tine
42. hearing	87. neat	132. tinge
43. heart	88. neath	133. tire
44. hearting	89. neigh	134. triage
45. heat	90. nightmare	135. trine

8

#5

How many words can you make from these 9 letters? Every word must contain the letter "E". You can use only these 9 letters and a letter cannot be used more than once in any word (you may use 2 A's). It's possible to make one 9-letter word.

Score: 20 words or more – EXCELLENT

    15 words or more – VERY GOOD

    10 words or more - GOOD

Hint: don't forget the plural forms of words, for example ear is 1 word and ears is a 2nd word. It's possible to make 160 words of 2 or more letters. (See following page for answers).

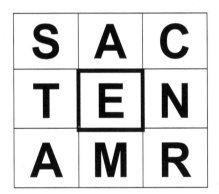

Answers:

1. ace	41. crane	81. nacres	121. seat
2. aces	42. cranes	82. nae	122. sec
3. acme	43. crate	83. name	123. secant
4. acne	44. crates	84. namer	124. sect
5. acre	45. cream	85. names	125. sen
6. acres	46. creams	86. nares	126. sent
7. amen	47. crest	87. near	127. sera
8. Antares	48. ear	88. nears	128. set
9. ante	49. earn	89. neat	129. smarten
10. antes	50. earns	90. nectar	130. smear
11. arcane	51. ears	91. nectars	131. snare
12. are	52. east	92. nest	132. stamen
13. area	53. eat	93. net	133. stance
14. areas	54. eats	94. nets	134. stare
15. arena	55. enact	95. race	135. steam
16. arenas	56. enacts	96. races	136. stem
17. Ares	57. era	97. rate	137. stern
18. ascent	58. mace	98. rates	138. sterna
19. aster	59. maces	99. react	139. stream
20. astern	60. mane	100. reacts	140. tame
21. ate	61. manes	101. ream	141. tamer
22. Caesar	62. manse	102. reams	142. tames
23. came	63. mantes	103. recant	143. tare
24. camera	64. mare	104. recants	144. tares
25. cane	65. mares	105. rent	145. tea
26. caner	66. marten	106. rents	146. team
27. canes	67. martens	107. rest	147. teams
28. canter	68. maser	108. sacrament	148. tear
29. canters	69. master	109. same	149. tears
30. care	70. mate	110. sane	150. teas
31. cares	71. mates	111. saner	151. ten
32. caret	72. me	112. sate	152. tens
33. carets	73. mean	113. scanter	153. term
34. case	74. means	114. scare	154. terms
35. caste	75. meant	115. scent	155. tern
36. caster	76. meat	116. scream	156. terns
37. cater	77. men	117. sea	157. trace
38. caters	78. mesa	118. seam	158. traces
39. cent	79. met	119. seaman	159. trance
40. cents	80. nacre	120. sear	160. trances

#6

How many words can you make from these 9 letters? Every word must contain the letter "E". You can use only these 9 letters and a letter cannot be used more than once in any word. It's possible to make three 9-letter words.

Score: 20 words or more – EXCELLENT
    15 words or more – VERY GOOD
    10 words or more - GOOD

It's possible to make 174 words of 2 or more letters. (See following page for answers).

Answers:

1. age	45. glare	89. large	133. regain
2. agent	46. glean	90. late	134. regal
3. agile	47. glen	91. later	135. reign
4. ale	48. granite	92. lathe	136. rein
5. alert	49. grate	93. lather	137. relating
6. alerting	50. great	94. lathering	138. renal
7. alien	51. hale	95. latrine	139. rent
8. aligner	52. haler	96. lea	140. rental
9. alter	53. halite	97. lean	141. retail
10. altering	54. halter	98. learn	142. retain
11. angel	55. haltering	99. learnt	143. retina
12. anger	56. hanger	100. leg	144. retinal
13. angle	57. hare	101. lei	145. rhea
14. ante	58. hate	102. length	146. rile
15. anther	59. hater	103. lent	147. ringlet
16. antler	60. he	104. let	148. rite
17. are	61. heal	105. liane	149. tale
18. argent	62. healing	106. lie	150. tangle
19. ate	63. hear	107. lien	151. tare
20. ear	64. hearing	108. lighten	152. tea
21. earl	65. heart	109. lighter	153. teal
22. earn	66. hearting	110. linage	154. tear
23. earth	67. heat	111. line	155. tearing
24. earthling	68. heating	112. linear	156. ten
25. eat	69. hegira	113. liner	157. tern
26. eating	70. heir	114. linger	158. thane
27. eight	71. hen	115. lire	159. the
28. elating	72. her	116. liter	160. their
29. entail	73. hernia	117. lithe	161. then
30. era	74. hinge	118. lither	162. thine
31. erg	75. hinter	119. litre	163. tie
32. gainer	76. hire	120. nae	164. tier
33. gaiter	77. ilea	121. nailer	165. tiger
34. gale	78. inert	122. near	166. tile
35. garnet	79. ingrate	123. neat	167. tiler
36. gate	80. inhale	124. neigh	168. tine
37. gather	81. inhaler	125. net	169. tinge
38. gear	82. inlet	126. niter	170. tingle
39. gel	83. integral	127. nitre	171. tire
40. gelatin	84. inter	128. rage	172. triage
41. genial	85. irate	129. range	173. triangle
42. genital	86. ire	130. rate	174. trine
43. gent	87. lager	131. ratline	
44. get	88. lane	132. real	

12

#7

How many words can you make from these 9 letters? Every word must contain the letter "E". You can use only these 9 letters and a letter cannot be used more than once in any word. It's possible to make one 9-letter word.

Score: 20 words or more – EXCELLENT

    15 words or more – VERY GOOD

    10 words or more - GOOD

It's possible to make 140 words of 3 or more letters. (See following page for answers).

Answers:

1. adieu	36. fade	71. gel	106. leg
2. afield	37. failed	72. geld	107. lei
3. afire	38. failure	73. gelid	108. lie
4. age	39. faired	74. gilder	109. lied
5. aged	40. fare	75. girdle	110. lieu
6. agile	41. fared	76. glade	111. life
7. ague	42. fear	77. glare	112. lifeguard
8. aide	43. fed	78. glared	113. lire
9. ailed	44. feral	79. glide	114. luge
10. aired	45. feud	80. glider	115. luger
11. alder	46. feudal	81. glue	116. lure
12. ale	47. fie	82. glued	117. lured
13. are	48. field	83. grade	118. rage
14. argue	49. figure	84. grief	119. raged
15. argued	50. figured	85. gruel	120. railed
16. auger	51. file	86. guide	121. read
17. dale	52. filed	87. guider	122. real
18. dare	53. fire	88. guilder	123. red
19. deaf	54. fired	89. guile	124. regal
20. deal	55. flare	90. gulfed	125. ride
21. dear	56. flared	91. idea	126. ridge
22. deli	57. flea	92. ideal	127. rife
23. derail	58. fled	93. idle	128. rifle
24. dialer	59. flied	94. idler	129. rifled
25. die	60. flier	95. ilea	130. rile
26. dire	61. flue	96. ire	131. riled
27. dirge	62. fragile	97. ireful	132. rude
28. due	63. fridge	98. lade	133. rue
29. duel	64. fried	99. lager	134. rued
30. ear	65. fudge	100. large	135. rule
31. earful	66. fuel	101. lauder	136. ruled
32. earl	67. furled	102. lea	137. uglier
33. elf	68. gale	103. lead	138. urea
34. era	69. gaudier	104. leaf	139. urge
35. erg	70. gear	105. led	140. urged

#8

How many words can you make from these 9 letters? There is no letter which must be used in every word. You can use only these 9 letters and a letter cannot be used more than once in any word. It's possible to make one 9-letter word.

Score: 20 words or more – EXCELLENT

    15 words or more – VERY GOOD

    10 words or more - GOOD

Hint: don't forget the plural forms of words, for example hen is 1 word and hens is a 2nd word. It's possible to make 124 words of 2 or more letters. (See following page for answers).

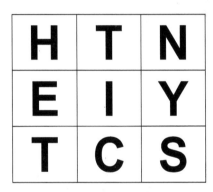

H	T	N
E	I	Y
T	C	S

Answers:

1. cent	32. ice	63. set	94. the
2. cents	33. ices	64. she	95. theist
3. chest	34. icy	65. shin	96. then
4. chi	35. in	66. shine	97. they
5. chin	36. incest	67. shiny	98. thin
6. chine	37. inch	68. shy	99. thins
7. chins	38. inches	69. sic	100. this
8. chit	39. ins	70. sin	101. thy
9. chits	40. insect	71. since	102. tic
10. cite	41. inset	72. sine	103. tics
11. cites	42. is	73. sit	104. tie
12. city	43. it	74. site	105. ties
13. cyst	44. itch	75. snit	106. tin
14. encyst	45. itches	76. snitch	107. tine
15. entity	46. its	77. stein	108. tines
16. etch	47. nest	78. stench	109. tins
17. ethic	48. net	79. stet	110. tint
18. ethics	49. nets	80. stint	111. tints
19. ethnic	50. nice	81. stitch	112. tiny
20. ethnics	51. nicest	82. sty	113. tit
21. he	52. nicety	83. sync	114. tithe
22. heist	53. niche	84. synch	115. tithes
23. hen	54. niches	85. synthetic	116. tits
24. hens	55. nit	86. ten	117. ye
25. hey	56. nits	87. tens	118. yen
26. hi	57. nitty	88. tent	119. yens
27. hint	58. scent	89. tenth	120. yes
28. hints	59. scythe	90. tenths	121. yet
29. his	60. sec	91. tents	122. yeti
30. hit	61. sect	92. test	123. yetis
31. hits	62. sent	93. testy	124. yin

#9

How many words can you make from these 9 letters? Every word must contain the letter "E". You can use only these 9 letters and a letter cannot be used more than once in any word. It's possible to make one 9-letter word.

Score: 20 words or more – EXCELLENT
    15 words or more – VERY GOOD
    10 words or more - GOOD

Hint: don't forget the plural forms of words, for example cue is 1 word and cues is a 2nd word. It's possible to make 168 words of 3 or more letters. (See following page for answers).

C	S	P
R	E	U
M	T	O

Answers: _____ _____ _____
_____ _____ _____ _____
_____ _____ _____ _____
_____ _____ _____ _____
_____ _____ _____ _____
_____ _____ _____ _____
_____ _____ _____ _____
_____ _____ _____ _____
_____ _____ _____ _____
_____ _____ _____ _____
_____ _____ _____ _____

1. cero	43. Eos	85. poster	127. set
2. ceros	44. Eros	86. posture	128. setup
3. come	45. eruct	87. pouter	129. smote
4. comer	46. eructs	88. pouters	130. some
5. comers	47. erupt	89. presto	131. sore
6. comes	48. erupts	90. proem	132. source
7. comet	49. escort	91. proems	133. spectrum
8. comets	50. met	92. prose	134. sperm
9. compute	51. mope	93. Proteus	135. spore
10. computer	52. mopes	94. pure	136. spouter
11. computers	53. more	95. purest	137. spruce
12. computes	54. mores	96. purse	138. spume
13. cope	55. mote	97. recoup	139. stem
14. copes	56. motes	98. recoups	140. step
15. copse	57. moue	99. recto	141. stomper
16. copter	58. mouse	100. rectos	142. store
17. copters	59. muse	101. rectum	143. stumper
18. core	60. muster	102. rectums	144. sue
19. cores	61. mute	103. rep	145. suet
20. corpse	62. muter	104. reps	146. super
21. corset	63. mutes	105. rest	147. sure
22. costume	64. ore	106. roe	148. tempo
23. cote	65. ouster	107. roes	149. tempos
24. cotes	66. outer	108. rope	150. term
25. course	67. per	109. ropes	151. terms
26. crept	68. perm	110. rose	152. toe
27. crest	69. perms	111. rote	153. toes
28. cruet	70. pert	112. rotes	154. tome
29. cruets	71. peso	113. rouse	155. tomes
30. crumpet	72. pest	114. route	156. toper
31. crumpets	73. pesto	115. routes	157. topers
32. cue	74. pet	116. rue	158. tore
33. cues	75. pets	117. rues	159. trope
34. cure	76. poem	118. ruse	160. tropes
35. cures	77. poems	119. scope	161. troupe
36. curse	78. poet	120. score	162. troupes
37. customer	79. poets	121. scoter	163. truce
38. cute	80. pore	122. sec	164. truces
39. cuter	81. pores	123. sect	165. true
40. ecru	82. pose	124. sector	166. upset
41. emu	83. poser	125. septum	167. use
42. emus	84. poseur	126. serum	168. user

18

#10

How many words can you make from these 9 letters? Every word must contain the letter "E". You can use only these 9 letters and a letter cannot be used more than once in any word (you may use 2 E's). It's possible to make one 9-letter word.

Score: 20 words or more – EXCELLENT

    15 words or more – VERY GOOD

    10 words or more - GOOD

It's possible to make 73 words of 3 or more letters. (See following page for answers).

Answers:

1.	abet	26.	eaglet	51.	lea
2.	able	27.	eat	52.	leave
3.	age	28.	eel	53.	lee
4.	ale	29.	elate	54.	leg
5.	alee	30.	elevate	55.	legate
6.	ate	31.	eta	56.	legatee
7.	bag	32.	eve	57.	let
8.	bagel	33.	gab	58.	levee
9.	bale	34.	gable	59.	tab
10.	bat	35.	Gael	60.	table
11.	bate	36.	gal	61.	tag
12.	beagle	37.	gale	62.	tale
13.	beat	38.	gate	63.	tea
14.	bee	39.	gave	64.	teal
15.	beet	40.	gavel	65.	tee
16.	beetle	41.	gee	66.	vale
17.	beg	42.	gel	67.	valet
18.	beget	43.	gelt	68.	vat
19.	belt	44.	get	69.	veal
20.	bet	45.	getable	70.	vegetable
21.	beta	46.	glee	71.	vegetal
22.	betel	47.	lab	72.	vela
23.	bevel	48.	lag	73.	vet
24.	bleat	49.	late		
25.	eagle	50.	lave		

#11

How many words can you make from these 9 letters? There is no letter which must be used in every word. You can use only these 9 letters and a letter cannot be used more than once in any word (you may use 2 E's and 2 I's). It's possible to make one 9-letter word.

Score: 20 words or more – EXCELLENT

    15 words or more – VERY GOOD

    10 words or more - GOOD

It's possible to make 74 words of 3 or more letters. (See following page for answers).

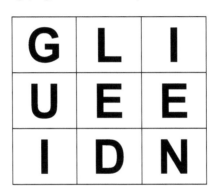

Answers:

1. deign	27. endue	53. leg
2. deli	28. gee	54. legend
3. deluge	29. gel	55. lei
4. den	30. geld	56. lend
5. dengue	31. gelid	57. lid
6. die	32. gene	58. lie
7. dieing	33. genie	59. lied
8. dig	34. gild	60. liege
9. din	35. gin	61. lien
10. dine	36. glee	62. lieu
11. ding	37. glen	63. line
12. due	38. glide	64. lined
13. duel	39. glue	65. lug
14. dueling	40. glued	66. luge
15. dug	41. gnu	67. lung
16. dun	42. guide	68. lunge
17. dune	43. <u>guideline</u>	69. lunged
18. dung	44. guild	70. nee
19. Eden	45. guile	71. need
20. edge	46. gun	72. nil
21. eel	47. idle	73. nude
22. elide	48. idling	74. nudge
23. eliding	49. indulge	
24. elude	50. led	
25. eluding	51. ledge	
26. end	52. lee	

#12

How many words can you make from these 9 letters? There is no letter which must be used in every word. You can use only these 9 letters and a letter cannot be used more than once in any word (you may use 2 E's). It's possible to make one 9-letter word.

Score: 20 words or more – EXCELLENT

    15 words or more – VERY GOOD

    10 words or more - GOOD

Hint: don't forget the plural forms of words, for example cue is 1 word and cues is a 2nd word. It's possible to make 151 words of 3 or more letters. (See following page for answers).

SCHEDULER

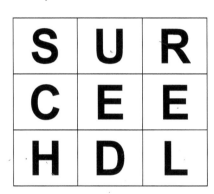

Answers: _____ _____ _____

_____ _____ _____

_____ _____ _____

_____ _____ _____

_____ _____ _____

_____ _____ _____

_____ _____ _____

_____ _____ _____

_____ _____ _____

_____ _____ _____

_____ _____ _____

_____ _____ _____

_____ _____ _____

23

1. cede	39. cursed	77. hurl	115. rush
2. cedes	40. deer	78. hurled	116. rushed
3. Ceres	41. deuce	79. hurls	117. schedule
4. cereus	42. deuces	80. lecher	118. <u>scheduler</u>
5. cheer	43. due	81. lechers	119. scree
6. cheers	44. duel	82. led	120. scud
7. churl	45. dueler	83. lee	121. sec
8. churls	46. duels	84. leech	122. seclude
9. clue	47. dues	85. leer	123. secure
10. clued	48. ecru	86. leers	124. secured
11. clues	49. educe	87. lees	125. seduce
12. Cree	50. educes	88. lucre	126. seducer
13. creed	51. eel	89. lurch	127. see
14. creeds	52. eels	90. lurched	128. seed
15. creel	53. elder	91. lurches	129. seer
16. creels	54. elders	92. lure	130. sere
17. Crees	55. else	93. lured	131. she
18. crude	56. elude	94. lures	132. shed
19. cruel	57. eludes	95. lush	133. sheer
20. crush	58. ere	96. recluse	134. shred
21. crushed	59. euchre	97. red	135. sled
22. cud	60. euchred	98. reds	136. slue
23. cue	61. euchres	99. reduce	137. slued
24. cued	62. heed	100. reduces	138. slur
25. cues	63. heeds	101. reed	139. such
26. cur	64. heel	102. reeds	140. sucre
27. curd	65. heels	103. reel	141. sue
28. curdle	66. held	104. reels	142. sued
29. curdles	67. her	105. rescue	143. suede
30. curds	68. Hercules	106. rescued	144. sure
31. cure	69. herd	107. rude	145. ulcer
32. cured	70. herds	108. rue	146. ulcers
33. cures	71. here	109. rued	147. use
34. curl	72. hers	110. rues	148. used
35. curled	73. hue	111. rule	149. user
36. curls	74. hues	112. ruled	150. usher
37. curs	75. hurdle	113. rules	151. ushered
38. curse	76. hurdles	114. ruse	

24

#13

How many words can you make from these 9 letters? There is no letter which must be used in every word. You can use only these 9 letters and a letter cannot be used more than once in any word (you may use 2 R's). It's possible to make one 9-letter word.

Score: 20 words or more – EXCELLENT

     15 words or more – VERY GOOD

     10 words or more - GOOD

Hint: don't forget the plural forms of words, for example ear is 1 word and ears is a 2nd word. It's possible to make 151 words of 3 or more letters. (See following page for answers).

A	R	G
M	E	I
B	R	S

Answers:

1. aegis	39. big	77. gem	115. raiser
2. age	40. bra	78. gems	116. ram
3. ageism	41. brag	79. germ	117. ramie
4. ages	42. brags	80. germs	118. rams
5. aim	43. braise	81. gibe	119. rare
6. aims	44. bras	82. giber	120. ream
7. air	45. brasier	83. gibes	121. reams
8. airs	46. bream	84. grab	122. rear
9. amber	47. breams	85. grabs	123. rears
10. ambergris	48. briar	86. gram	124. rib
11. are	49. briars	87. grams	125. ribs
12. Aries	50. brier	88. grim	126. rig
13. arise	51. briers	89. grime	127. rigs
14. arm	52. brig	90. grimes	128. rim
15. armies	53. brigs	91. iamb	129. rime
16. arms	54. brim	92. iambs	130. rimes
17. bag	55. brims	93. image	131. rims
18. bags	56. ear	94. images	132. rise
19. bar	57. ears	95. ire	133. riser
20. bare	58. emir	96. magi	134. saber
21. barer	59. era	97. mar	135. sabre
22. bares	60. erg	98. mare	136. sag
23. barge	61. ergs	99. mares	137. sage
24. barges	62. err	100. marries	138. sager
25. bars	63. errs	101. mars	139. same
26. base	64. gab	102. maser	140. sari
27. baser	65. gabs	103. mesa	141. sea
28. beam	66. game	104. mirage	142. seam
29. beams	67. gamer	105. mirages	143. sear
30. bear	68. games	106. mire	144. semi
31. bears	69. gamier	107. mires	145. sera
32. beg	70. gar	108. miser	146. Serb
33. begs	71. garb	109. rabies	147. sierra
34. berm	72. garbs	110. rag	148. sigma
35. berms	73. gars	111. rage	149. sir
36. bias	74. gas	112. rages	150. sire
37. bier	75. gear	113. rags	151. smear
38. biers	76. gears	114. raise	

am•ber•gris (ăm′bər-grĭs′, -grēs′) *n.* A waxy, grayish substance formed in the intestines of sperm whales and found floating at sea or washed ashore. It is added to perfumes to slow down the rate of evaporation.

#14

How many words can you make from these 9 letters? There is no letter which must be used in every word. You can use only these 9 letters and a letter cannot be used more than once in any word (you may use 2 R's). It's possible to make one 9-letter word.

Score: 20 words or more – EXCELLENT

    15 words or more – VERY GOOD

    10 words or more - GOOD

Hint: don't forget the plural forms of words, for example err is 1 word and errs is a 2nd word. It's possible to make 77 words of 3 or more letters. (See following page for answers).

S	R	K
R	I	F
W	E	O

F
I
R
E
W
O
R
K
S

Answers:

_____ _____ _____
_____ _____ _____
_____ _____ _____
_____ _____ _____
_____ _____ _____
_____ _____ _____
_____ _____ _____
_____ _____ _____
_____ _____ _____
_____ _____ _____
_____ _____ _____

1. eros	27. kerf	53. sore
2. err	28. kerfs	54. sorer
3. errs	29. ore	55. sow
4. few	30. osier	56. sower
5. fie	31. owe	57. swore
6. fir	32. owes	58. weir
7. fire	33. rife	59. weirs
8. firer	34. rifer	60. wife
9. fires	35. rise	61. wire
10. fireworks	36. riser	62. wires
11. firs	37. risk	63. wise
12. foe	38. roe	64. wiser
13. foes	39. roes	65. woe
14. for	40. rose	66. woes
15. fore	41. rosier	67. wok
16. fork	42. row	68. woke
17. forks	43. rower	69. woks
18. fries	44. rows	70. wore
19. frisk	45. serf	71. work
20. frisker	46. serif	72. worker
21. fro	47. sew	73. workers
22. frowsier	48. sir	74. works
23. ifs	49. sire	75. worries
24. ire	50. skew	76. worse
25. irk	51. ski	77. wrier
26. irks	52. skier	

#15

How many words can you make from these 9 letters? Every word must contain the letter "E". You can use only these 9 letters and a letter cannot be used more than once in a word. It's possible to make one 9-letter word.

Score: 20 words or more – EXCELLENT
    15 words or more – VERY GOOD
    10 words or more - GOOD

It's possible to make 93 words of 3 or more letters. (See following page for answers).

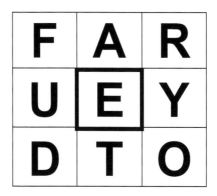

Answers: _____ _____ _____
_____ _____ _____
_____ _____ _____
_____ _____ _____
_____ _____ _____
_____ _____ _____
_____ _____ _____
_____ _____ _____
_____ _____ _____
_____ _____ _____
_____ _____ _____
_____ _____ _____
_____ _____ _____

1. adore	32. fate	63. ready
2. after	33. fated	64. red
3. are	34. fear	65. rode
4. ate	35. feat	66. roe
5. aye	36. fed	67. rote
6. dafter	37. fedora	68. route
7. dare	38. feta	69. routed
8. date	39. feud	70. rude
9. dater	40. <u>feudatory</u>	71. rue
10. deaf	41. fey	72. rued
11. dear	42. foe	73. rye
12. defray	43. forayed	74. tare
13. deft	44. fore	75. tea
14. defy	45. forte	76. tear
15. detour	46. foyer	77. teary
16. doe	47. frayed	78. toe
17. doer	48. fret	79. toed
18. dote	49. Frey	80. tore
19. doter	50. oared	81. toured
20. due	51. ode	82. toyed
21. duet	52. orate	83. trade
22. dye	53. orated	84. tread
23. dyer	54. ore	85. trey
24. ear	55. outed	86. true
25. eat	56. outer	87. trued
26. era	57. rafted	88. tyre
27. fade	58. rate	89. urea
28. fadeout	59. rated	90. yea
29. faery	60. rayed	91. year
30. fare	61. read	92. yet
31. fared	62. readout	93. yore

feu·da·to·ry (fy$\overline{oo}$′də-tôr′ē, -tōr′ē) *n.*, *pl.* **feu·da·to·ries. 1.** A person holding land by feudal fee; a vassal. **2.** A feudal fee. --**feu·da·to·ry** *adj.* **1.** Of, relating to, or characteristic of the feudal relationship between vassal and lord. **2.** Owing feudal homage or allegiance.

#16

How many words can you make from these 9 letters? There is no letter which must be used in every word. You can use only these 9 letters and a letter cannot be used more than once in any word (you may use 2 A's). It's possible to make one 9-letter word.

Score: 20 words or more – EXCELLENT

15 words or more – VERY GOOD

10 words or more - GOOD

It's possible to make 115 words of 3 or more letters. (See following page for answers).

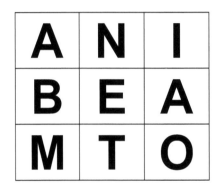

Answers: _____ _____ _____ _____

_____ _____ _____ _____

_____ _____ _____ _____

_____ _____ _____ _____

_____ _____ _____ _____

_____ _____ _____ _____

_____ _____ _____ _____

_____ _____ _____ _____

_____ _____ _____ _____

_____ _____ _____ _____

_____ _____ _____ _____

_____ _____ _____ _____

_____ _____ _____ _____

_____ _____ _____ _____

_____ _____ _____ _____

1. abate	40. biota	79. moat
2. abeam	41. bit	80. mob
3. abet	42. bite	81. mot
4. <u>abominate</u>	43. boa	82. mote
5. aim	44. boat	83. nab
6. ambient	45. boatman	84. nae
7. ambit	46. boatmen	85. name
8. ameba	47. bone	86. neat
9. amen	48. eat	87. neb
10. amine	49. emit	88. net
11. amoeba	50. entomb	89. nib
12. anemia	51. eon	90. nit
13. animate	52. iamb	91. not
14. animato	53. Ibo	92. note
15. ant	54. inmate	93. oat
16. ante	55. into	94. obi
17. anti	56. ion	95. obit
18. ate	57. iota	96. obtain
19. atom	58. item	97. omen
20. atone	59. main	98. omit
21. baa	60. man	99. one
22. bait	61. mane	100. tab
23. ban	62. mania	101. tame
24. bane	63. manta	102. tan
25. bantam	64. mat	103. tea
26. bat	65. mate	104. team
27. bate	66. mean	105. ten
28. baton	67. meant	106. tie
29. beam	68. meat	107. time
30. bean	69. men	108. tin
31. beano	70. met	109. tine
32. beat	71. mien	110. toe
33. bemoan	72. min	111. tom
34. bent	73. mina	112. tomb
35. bet	74. mine	113. tome
36. beta	75. mint	114. ton
37. bin	76. mite	115. tone
38. bio	77. Moabite	
39. biome	78. moan	

a·bom·i·nate (ə-bŏm′ə-nāt′) *tr.v.* **a·bom·i·nat·ed,**
a·bom·i·nat·ing, **a·bom·i·nates**. To detest
thoroughly; abhor. **--a·bom′i·na′tor** *n.*

#17

How many words can you make from these 9 letters? There is no letter which must be used in every word. You can use only these 9 letters and a letter cannot be used more than once in any word (you may use 2 I's). It's possible to make one 9-letter word.

Score: 20 words or more – EXCELLENT

    15 words or more – VERY GOOD

    10 words or more - GOOD

It's possible to make 123 words of 3 or more letters. (See following page for answers).

A	R	O
G	E	N
I	I	B

Answers:

1. aborigine	42. bong	83. ignore
2. age	43. bore	84. ion
3. ago	44. boring	85. ire
4. air	45. born	86. iron
5. airing	46. borne	87. nab
6. anger	47. bra	88. nae
7. are	48. brag	89. nag
8. argon	49. brain	90. near
9. bag	50. bran	91. neb
10. ban	51. brig	92. Negro
11. bane	52. brine	93. nib
12. bang	53. bring	94. nor
13. bar	54. brio	95. oar
14. bare	55. brogan	96. oaring
15. barge	56. ear	97. obi
16. baring	57. earn	98. ogre
17. barn	58. ego	99. one
18. baron	59. eon	100. orange
19. bean	60. era	101. orb
20. beano	61. erg	102. ore
21. bear	62. ergo	103. organ
22. bearing	63. gab	104. origin
23. beg	64. gain	105. Rabi
24. began	65. gainer	106. rag
25. begin	66. gar	107. rage
26. begonia	67. garb	108. rain
27. being	68. gear	109. ran
28. bier	69. gibe	110. rang
29. big	70. giber	111. range
30. bin	71. gin	112. regain
31. binge	72. gob	113. region
32. binger	73. gone	114. reign
33. bingo	74. goner	115. rein
34. bio	75. gore	116. rib
35. boa	76. grab	117. rig
36. boar	77. grain	118. ring
37. Boer	78. grin	119. roan
38. bog	79. groan	120. rob
39. bogie	80. groin	121. robe
40. bone	81. Ibo	122. robin
41. boner	82. Igbo	123. roe

ab·o·rig·i·ne (ăb′ə-rĭj′ə-nē) *n.* **1.** A member of the indigenous or earliest known population of a region. **2. aborigines**. The flora and fauna native to a geographic area.

#18

How many words can you make from these 9 letters? There is no letter which must be used in every word. You can use only these 9 letters and a letter cannot be used more than once in any word (you may use 2 L's and 2 A's). It's possible to make one 9-letter word.

Score: 20 words or more – EXCELLENT

    15 words or more – VERY GOOD

    10 words or more - GOOD

Hint: don't forget the plural forms of words, for example ail is 1 word and ails is a 2nd word. It's possible to make 93 words of 3 or more letters. (See following page for answers).

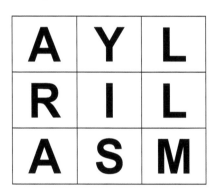

Answers:

1. ail	32. lama	63. rail
2. ails	33. lamas	64. rails
3. aim	34. lams	65. rally
4. aims	35. lay	66. ram
5. air	36. lays	67. rams
6. airs	37. liar	68. ray
7. airy	38. liars	69. rays
8. ala	39. lily	70. rill
9. alarm	40. limy	71. rills
10. alarms	41. lira	72. rim
11. alas	42. llama	73. rims
12. alias	43. llamas	74. rimy
13. all	44. mail	75. riyal
14. allay	45. mails	76. sail
15. allays	46. Malay	77. salami
16. ally	47. Malays	78. salary
17. alms	48. mall	79. sally
18. amaryllis	49. malls	80. sari
19. aria	50. mar	81. say
20. arias	51. marl	82. sill
21. aril	52. marls	83. silly
22. arils	53. marly	84. sir
23. arm	54. mars	85. slam
24. arms	55. may	86. slay
25. army	56. Maya	87. slim
26. ill	57. Mayas	88. slimly
27. ills	58. mil	89. slimy
28. Islam	59. mill	90. sly
29. lair	60. mills	91. small
30. lairs	61. mils	92. yam
31. lam	62. mislay	93. yams

am·a·ryl·lis (ăm′ə-rĭl′ĭs) *n.* **1.** Any of several chiefly tropical American bulbous plants of the genus *Hippeastrum* grown as ornamentals for their large, showy, funnel-shaped, variously colored flowers that are grouped in umbels. **2.** See **belladonna lily**. **3.** Any of several similar or related plants. **4. Amaryllis**. Used in classical pastoral poetry as a conventional name for a shepherdess.

#19

How many words can you make from these 9 letters? There is no letter which must be used in every word. You can use only these 9 letters and a letter cannot be used more than once in any word (you may use 2 I's). It's possible to make one 9-letter word.

Score: 20 words or more – EXCELLENT

15 words or more – VERY GOOD

10 words or more - GOOD

It's possible to make 121 words of 3 or more letters. (See following page for answers).

M	A	I
R	O	T
G	N	I

Answers:

1. ago	32. grit	63. moan	94. riot
2. aim	33. groan	64. moat	95. rioting
3. aiming	34. groin	65. morn	96. roam
4. air	35. imago	66. mot	97. roaming
5. airing	36. ingot	67. nag	98. roan
6. amigo	37. into	68. nit	99. Roman
7. among	38. ion	69. nor	100. rot
8. ant	39. iota	70. norm	101. tag
9. anti	40. iron	71. not	102. taming
10. argon	41. magi	72. oar	103. tan
11. argot	42. main	73. oaring	104. tang
12. arm	43. man	74. oat	105. tango
13. arming	44. mango	75. omit	106. tar
14. art	45. manor	76. orating	107. tarn
15. atom	46. Maori	77. organ	108. taro
16. gain	47. mar	78. origami	109. timing
17. gait	48. margin	79. origin	110. tin
18. gamin	49. mart	80. rag	111. tiring
19. gar	50. martin	81. rain	112. tog
20. gator	51. martini	82. ram	113. toga
21. giant	52. mat	83. ran	114. tom
22. gin	53. mating	84. rang	115. ton
23. girt	54. matron	85. rant	116. torn
24. gnat	55. migrant	86. rat	117. train
25. goat	56. <u>migration</u>	87. rating	118. tram
26. got	57. min	88. ratio	119. trig
27. grain	58. mina	89. ration	120. trim
28. gram	59. mini	90. rig	121. trio
29. grant	60. minor	91. rim	
30. grim	61. mint	92. riming	
31. grin	62. miring	93. ring	

mi·grate (mī′grāt′) *intr.v.* **mi·grat·ed, mi·grat·ing, mi·grates**. **1.** To move from one country or region and settle in another. **2.** To change location periodically, especially by moving seasonally from one region to another. **--mi"gra"tor** *n.* **mi·gra·tion** *n.*, The act or an instance of migrating.

#20

How many words can you make from these 9 letters? There is no letter which must be used in every word. You can use only these 9 letters and a letter cannot be used more than once in any word (you may use 2 A's). It's possible to make one 9-letter word.

Score: 20 words or more – EXCELLENT

    15 words or more – VERY GOOD

    10 words or more - GOOD

Hint: don't forget the plural forms of words, for example drug is 1 word and drugs is a 2nd word. It's possible to make 144 words of 3 or more letters. (See following page for answers).

G	S	N
U	A	I
R	D	A

Answers:

_____ _____ _____ _____

_____ _____ _____ _____

_____ _____ _____ _____

_____ _____ _____ _____

_____ _____ _____ _____

_____ _____ _____ _____

_____ _____ _____ _____

_____ _____ _____ _____

_____ _____ _____ _____

_____ _____ _____ _____

_____ _____ _____ _____

_____ _____ _____ _____

1. ads	37. dugs	73. ids	109. rugs
2. again	38. dun	74. iguana	110. ruin
3. agar	39. dung	75. iguanas	111. ruing
4. aid	40. duns	76. Indus	112. ruins
5. aids	41. during	77. ins	113. run
6. Ainu	42. gad	78. nadir	114. rung
7. Ainus	43. gads	79. nag	115. rungs
8. air	44. gain	80. nags	116. runs
9. airs	45. gains	81. naiad	117. sad
10. and	46. gar	82. naiads	118. sag
11. anus	47. gars	83. nard	119. saga
12. aria	48. gas	84. nurd	120. said
13. arias	49. gin	85. nurds	121. San
14. arid	50. gins	86. rad	122. sand
15. Asian	51. gird	87. radian	123. sang
16. aura	52. girds	88. radians	124. sangria
17. auras	53. gnu	89. radius	125. saran
18. dais	54. grad	90. rads	126. sari
19. daring	55. grads	91. rag	127. sauna
20. darn	56. grain	92. rags	128. sign
21. darns	57. grains	93. raid	129. sin
22. dig	58. grand	94. raids	130. sing
23. digs	59. grid	95. rain	131. Sir
24. din	60. grids	96. rains	132. sir
25. dinar	61. grin	97. ran	133. snag
26. ding	62. grind	98. rand	134. snug
27. dings	63. grinds	99. rang	135. sugar
28. dingus	64. grins	100. rid	136. suing
29. dins	65. guar	101. rids	137. sun
30. drag	66. guard	102. rig	138. sung
31. drags	67. guardian	103. rigs	139. Ugrian
32. drain	68. guardians	104. rind	140. Ugrians
33. drains	69. guards	105. rinds	141. unsaid
34. drug	70. guars	106. ring	142. urn
35. drugs	71. gun	107. rings	143. urns
36. dug	72. guns	108. rug	144. using

#21

How many words can you make from these 9 letters? There is no letter which must be used in every word. You can use only these 9 letters and a letter cannot be used more than once in any word (you may use 2 C's and 2 I's). It's possible to make one 9-letter word.

Score: 20 words or more – EXCELLENT

15 words or more – VERY GOOD

10 words or more - GOOD

Hint: don't forget the plural forms of words, for example face is 1 word and faces is a 2nd word. It's possible to make 76 words of 3 or more letters. (See following page for answers).

F
R
I
C
C
A
S
I
E

Answers:

1. ace	27. era	53. races
2. aces	28. face	54. raise
3. acre	29. faces	55. rice
4. acres	30. fair	56. rices
5. afire	31. fairies	57. rife
6. air	32. fairs	58. rise
7. airs	33. far	59. sac
8. arc	34. farce	60. <u>sacrifice</u>
9. arcs	35. farces	61. safe
10. are	36. fare	62. safer
11. Ares	37. fares	63. sari
12. Aries	38. fear	64. scar
13. arise	39. fears	65. scarce
14. cafe	40. fie	66. scare
15. cafes	41. fir	67. scarf
16. car	42. fire	68. sea
17. care	43. fires	69. sear
18. cares	44. firs	70. sec
19. caries	45. fries	71. sera
20. cars	46. ice	72. serf
21. case	47. ices	73. serif
22. cir	48. icier	74. sic
23. circa	49. ifs	75. sir
24. cries	50. ire	76. sire
25. ear	51. iris	
26. ears	52. race	

#22

How many words can you make from these 9 letters? There is no letter which must be used in every word. You can use only these 9 letters and a letter cannot be used more than once in any word. It's possible to make one 9-letter word.

Score: 20 words or more – EXCELLENT

    15 words or more – VERY GOOD

    10 words or more - GOOD

Hint: don't forget the plural forms of words, for example bar is 1 word and bars is a 2nd word. It's possible to make 236 words of 3 or more letters. (See following page for answers).

M	A	R
N	E	I
B	S	U

Answers:

1.	abuse	49.	berms	97.	inure	145.	number	193.	saber
2.	abuser	50.	bias	98.	inures	146.	numbers	194.	same
3.	aim	51.	bier	99.	ire	147.	numbs	195.	sane
4.	aims	52.	biers	100.	ism	148.	nurse	196.	saner
5.	Ainu	53.	bin	101.	main	149.	rabies	197.	sari
6.	air	54.	bins	102.	mains	150.	rain	198.	sea
7.	airmen	55.	bra	103.	man	151.	rains	199.	seam
8.	airs	56.	brain	104.	mane	152.	raise	200.	sear
9.	amber	57.	brains	105.	manes	153.	ram	201.	semi
10.	amen	58.	braise	106.	mans	154.	ramie	202.	seminar
11.	amine	59.	bran	107.	manse	155.	rams	203.	sera
12.	amuse	60.	bras	108.	manure	156.	ran	204.	Serb
13.	amuser	61.	bream	109.	manures	157.	ream	205.	Serbian
14.	aneurism	62.	breams	110.	mar	158.	reams	206.	serum
15.	animus	63.	brim	111.	mare	159.	rebus	207.	sin
16.	anise	64.	brims	112.	mares	160.	rein	208.	sine
17.	anus	65.	brine	113.	marine	161.	reins	209.	sir
18.	are	66.	brines	114.	marines	162.	remain	210.	sire
19.	Ares	67.	bruin	115.	mars	163.	remains	211.	siren
20.	Aries	68.	bruins	116.	maser	164.	resin	212.	smear
21.	arise	69.	bruise	117.	mean	165.	rib	213.	snare
22.	arisen	70.	bum	118.	means	166.	ribs	214.	snub
23.	arm	71.	bums	119.	men	167.	rim	215.	sub
24.	armies	72.	bun	120.	menu	168.	rime	216.	submarine
25.	arms	73.	buns	121.	mesa	169.	rimes	217.	sue
26.	ban	74.	bur	122.	mien	170.	rims	218.	sum
27.	bane	75.	buries	123.	miens	171.	rinse	219.	sun
28.	bans	76.	burn	124.	mine	172.	rise	220.	sunbeam
29.	bar	77.	burns	125.	mines	173.	risen	221.	sure
30.	bare	78.	burs	126.	minus	174.	rub	222.	surname
31.	bares	79.	bursa	127.	mire	175.	rube	223.	umbra
32.	barium	80.	bus	128.	mires	176.	rubes	224.	umbrae
33.	barmen	81.	busier	129.	miser	177.	rubies	225.	unbar
34.	barn	82.	ear	130.	muse	178.	rubs	226.	unbars
35.	barns	83.	earn	131.	nab	179.	rue	227.	urban
36.	bars	84.	earns	132.	nabs	180.	rues	228.	urbane
37.	base	85.	ears	133.	name	181.	ruin	229.	urea
38.	baser	86.	emir	134.	names	182.	ruins	230.	uremia
39.	basin	87.	era	135.	near	183.	rum	231.	urine
40.	beam	88.	erbium	136.	nears	184.	rumba	232.	urn
41.	beams	89.	iamb	137.	neb	185.	rumen	233.	urns
42.	bean	90.	iambs	138.	nebs	186.	rumens	234.	ursine
43.	beans	91.	iambus	139.	nib	187.	rums	235.	use
44.	bear	92.	imbue	140.	nibs	188.	run	236.	user
45.	bears	93.	imbues	141.	nimbus	189.	rune		
46.	beau	94.	ins	142.	nub	190.	runes		
47.	beaus	95.	inseam	143.	nubs	191.	runs		
48.	berm	96.	insure	144.	numb	192.	ruse		

#23

How many words can you make from these 9 letters? There is no letter which must be used in every word. You can use only these 9 letters and a letter cannot be used more than once in any word (you may use 2 T's and 2 I's). It's possible to make one 9-letter word.

Score: 20 words or more – EXCELLENT

    15 words or more – VERY GOOD

    10 words or more - GOOD

Hint: don't forget the plural forms of words, for example ant is 1 word and ants is a 2nd word. It's possible to make 82 words of 3 or more letters. (See following page for answers).

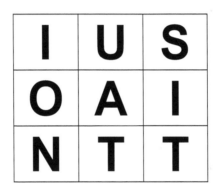

Answers:

_____   _____   _____   _____

_____   _____   _____   _____

_____   _____   _____   _____

_____   _____   _____   _____

_____   _____   _____   _____

_____   _____   _____   _____

_____   _____   _____   _____

_____   _____   _____   _____

_____   _____   _____   _____

_____   _____   _____   _____

_____   _____   _____   _____

_____   _____   _____   _____

1. Ainu
2. Ainus
3. ant
4. anti
5. ants
6. anus
7. aunt
8. auto
9. autos
10. ins
11. into
12. intuit
13. intuits
14. Inuit
15. Inuits
16. ion
17. iota
18. its
19. nit
20. nits
21. not
22. nut
23. nuts
24. oat
25. oats
26. onus
27. oust
28. out

29. outs
30. saint
31. sat
32. satin
33. sin
34. sit
35. situation
36. snit
37. snot
38. snout
39. son
40. sot
41. stain
42. stat
43. station
44. stint
45. stoat
46. stout
47. stun
48. stunt
49. suit
50. sun
51. taint
52. taints
53. tan
54. tans
55. Taoist
56. tat

57. tats
58. taunt
59. taunts
60. taut
61. tin
62. tins
63. tint
64. tints
65. tit
66. Titan
67. Titans
68. tits
69. Titus
70. toast
71. ton
72. tons
73. tot
74. tots
75. tout
76. touts
77. tuition
78. tuna
79. tunas
80. unit
81. units
82. unto

#24

How many words can you make from these 9 letters? There is no letter which must be used in every word. You can use only these 9 letters and a letter cannot be used more than once in any word (you may use 2 R's and 2 A's). It's possible to make one 9-letter word.

Score: 20 words or more – EXCELLENT

15 words or more – VERY GOOD

10 words or more - GOOD

It's possible to make 95 words of 3 or more letters. (See following page for answers).

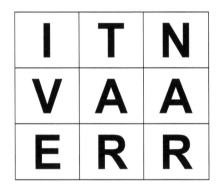

I	T	N
V	A	A
E	R	R

Answers:

1. air	33. nave	65. tarn
2. ant	34. near	66. tavern
3. ante	35. neat	67. tea
4. anti	36. net	68. tear
5. are	37. nit	69. ten
6. area	38. niter	70. tern
7. arena	39. nitre	71. terrain
8. arrant	40. rain	72. tiara
9. arrive	41. ran	73. tie
10. art	42. rant	74. tier
11. artier	43. ranter	75. tin
12. ate	44. rare	76. tine
13. atria	45. rat	77. tire
14. aver	46. rate	78. train
15. avert	47. rave	79. trainer
16. avian	48. raven	80. trine
17. ear	49. ravine	81. vain
18. earn	50. rear	82. vainer
19. eat	51. rein	83. van
20. era	52. rent	84. vane
21. err	53. reran	85. variant
22. errant	54. retain	86. vat
23. errata	55. retina	87. vein
24. inert	56. rev	88. vena
25. inter	57. rite	89. vent
26. invert	58. rive	90. vet
27. irate	59. riven	91. via
28. ire	60. river	92. vie
29. naive	61. rivet	93. vine
30. narrate	62. tan	94. vita
31. narrative	63. tar	95. vitae
32. native	64. tare	

#25

How many words can you make from these 9 letters? There is no letter which must be used in every word. You can use only these 9 letters and a letter cannot be used more than once in any word (you may use 2 N's and 2 S's). It's possible to make two 9-letter words.

Score: 20 words or more – EXCELLENT

    15 words or more – VERY GOOD

    10 words or more - GOOD

Hint: don't forget the plural forms of words, for example ace is 1 word and aces is a 2nd word. It's possible to make 154 words of 3 or more letters. (See following page for answers).

I	N	C
N	A	T
E	S	S

Answers:

1. ace	40. castes	79. nets	118. sic
2. aces	41. casts	80. nice	119. sienna
3. acne	42. cat	81. nicest	120. siesta
4. act	43. cats	82. nine	121. sin
5. acts	44. cent	83. nines	122. since
6. ancient	45. cents	84. nit	123. sine
7. ancients	46. cite	85. nits	124. sins
8. anent	47. cites	86. sac	125. sis
9. anise	48. east	87. sacs	126. sit
10. anises	49. eat	88. saint	127. site
11. ant	50. eats	89. saints	128. sites
12. ante	51. enact	90. sane	129. sits
13. antes	52. enacts	91. sanest	130. snit
14. anti	53. ice	92. sans	131. snits
15. antic	54. ices	93. sat	132. stain
16. antics	55. inane	94. sate	133. stains
17. antis	56. inanest	95. sates	134. stance
18. ants	57. Inca	96. satin	135. stances
19. ascent	58. Incas	97. satins	136. stein
20. ascents	59. incase	98. scan	137. steins
21. ass	60. incessant	99. scans	138. sties
22. assent	61. incest	100. scant	139. tan
23. asset	62. inn	101. scants	140. tans
24. ate	63. innate	102. scat	141. tansies
25. can	64. inns	103. scats	142. tea
26. cane	65. ins	104. scent	143. teas
27. canes	66. insane	105. scents	144. ten
28. canine	67. insect	106. sea	145. tennis
29. canines	68. insects	107. seas	146. tens
30. canniest	69. inset	108. seat	147. tic
31. cans	70. insets	109. seats	148. tics
32. canst	71. instance	110. sec	149. tie
33. cant	72. instances	111. secant	150. ties
34. cants	73. its	112. sect	151. tin
35. case	74. nascent	113. sects	152. tine
36. casein	75. neat	114. sen	153. tines
37. cases	76. nest	115. sent	154. tins
38. cast	77. nests	116. set	
39. caste	78. net	117. sets	

in·ces·sant (ĭn-sĕs′ənt) *adj.* Continuing without interruption. **--in·ces′san·cy** *n.* **--in·ces′sant·ly** *adv.*

#26

How many words can you make from these 9 letters? There is no letter which must be used in every word. You can use only these 9 letters and a letter cannot be used more than once in any word. It's possible to make one 9-letter word.

Score: 20 words or more – EXCELLENT

15 words or more – VERY GOOD

10 words or more - GOOD

Hint: don't forget the plural forms of words, for example ace is 1 word and aces is a 2nd word. It's possible to make 155 words of 3 or more letters. (See following page for answers).

O	B	F
A	E	T
U	S	C

Answers:

1. abet	40. bouts	79. faces	118. sat
2. abets	41. bus	80. facet	119. sate
3. about	42. bust	81. facets	120. sauce
4. abuse	43. but	82. fact	121. scab
5. abut	44. buteo	83. facts	122. scat
6. abuts	45. buteos	84. fast	123. Scot
7. ace	46. cab	85. fat	124. scout
8. aces	47. cabs	86. fate	125. scuba
9. act	48. cafe	87. fates	126. sea
10. acts	49. cafes	88. fats	127. seat
11. acute	50. case	89. faucet	128. sec
12. aft	51. cast	90. faucets	129. sect
13. ascot	52. caste	91. Faust	130. set
14. ate	53. cat	92. feast	131. sob
15. auto	54. cats	93. feat	132. sofa
16. autos	55. cause	94. feats	133. soft
17. base	56. coast	95. feta	134. sot
18. baste	57. coat	96. fetus	135. stab
19. bat	58. coats	97. fob	136. stub
20. bate	59. cob	98. fobs	137. sub
21. bates	60. cobs	99. focus	138. sue
22. bats	61. cost	100. foe	139. suet
23. beast	62. cot	101. foes	140. tab
24. beat	63. cote	102. foetus	141. tabs
25. beats	64. cotes	103. fuse	142. taco
26. beau	65. cots	104. oaf	143. tacos
27. beaus	66. cub	105. oafs	144. tea
28. beaut	67. cube	106. oat	145. teas
29. besot	68. cubes	107. oats	146. toe
30. best	69. cubs	108. <u>obfuscate</u>	147. toes
31. bet	70. cue	109. obtuse	148. tofu
32. beta	71. cues	110. oft	149. tub
33. bets	72. cut	111. oust	150. tuba
34. boa	73. cute	112. out	151. tube
35. boas	74. cuts	113. outface	152. tubes
36. boast	75. east	114. outfaces	153. tubs
37. boat	76. eat	115. outs	154. use
38. boats	77. eats	116. sac	155. Ute
39. bout	78. face	117. safe	

ob·fus·cate (ŏb′fə-skāt′, ŏb-fŭs′kāt′) *tr.v.* **ob·fus·cat·ed**, **ob·fus·cat·ing**, **ob·fus·cates**. **1.** To make so confused or opaque as to be difficult to perceive or understand. **2.** To render indistinct or dim; darken. **--ob′fus·ca′tion** *n.* **-- ob·fus′ca·to′ry** (ŏb-fŭs′kə-tôr′ē, -tōr′ē, əb-) *adj.*

#27

How many words can you make from these 9 letters? There is no letter which must be used in every word. You can use only these 9 letters and a letter cannot be used more than once in any word (you may use 2 I's). It's possible to make one 9-letter word.

Score: 20 words or more – EXCELLENT

     15 words or more – VERY GOOD

     10 words or more - GOOD

It's possible to make 194 words of 3 or more letters. (See following page for answers).

R	G	N
L	E	I
I	A	T

Answers:

1. age	50. genial	99. lent	148. retail
2. agent	51. genital	100. let	149. retailing
3. agile	52. gent	101. liar	150. retain
4. ail	53. get	102. lie	151. retina
5. ailing	54. giant	103. lien	152. retinal
6. air	55. gilt	104. lignite	153. rig
7. airing	56. gin	105. linage	154. rile
8. airline	57. girl	106. line	155. riling
9. ale	58. girt	107. linear	156. ring
10. alert	59. glare	108. liner	157. ringlet
11. alerting	60. glean	109. linger	158. rite
12. alien	61. glen	110. lint	159. tag
13. align	62. glint	111. lira	160. tail
14. aligner	63. gnarl	112. lire	161. tailing
15. alit	64. gnat	113. liter	162. tale
16. alter	65. grail	114. litre	163. tan
17. altering	66. grain	115. nag	164. tang
18. angel	67. granite	116. nail	165. tangle
19. anger	68. grant	117. nailer	166. tar
20. angle	69. grate	118. near	167. tare
21. ant	70. great	119. neat	168. tarn
22. ante	71. grin	120. net	169. tea
23. anti	72. grit	121. nil	170. teal
24. antler	73. ignite	122. nit	171. tear
25. are	74. igniter	123. niter	172. tearing
26. argent	75. ilea	124. nitre	173. ten
27. art	76. inert	125. rag	174. tern
28. ate	77. inertia	126. rage	175. tie
29. ear	78. inertial	127. rail	176. tier
30. earl	79. ingrate	128. railing	177. tiger
31. earn	80. inlet	129. rain	178. tile
32. eat	81. integral	130. ran	179. tiling
33. eating	82. inter	131. rang	180. tin
34. elating	83. irate	132. range	181. tine
35. entail	84. ire	133. rant	182. tinge
36. era	85. lag	134. rat	183. tingle
37. erg	86. lager	135. rate	184. tingler
38. gain	87. lain	136. rating	185. tinier
39. gainer	88. lair	137. ratline	186. tire
40. gait	89. lane	138. real	187. tiring
41. gaiter	90. large	139. regain	188. trail
42. gal	91. late	140. regal	189. trailing
43. gale	92. later	141. reign	190. train
44. gar	93. Latin	142. rein	191. triage
45. garnet	94. latrine	143. relating	192. trial
46. gate	95. lea	144. reliant	193. triangle
47. gear	96. lean	145. renal	194. trig
48. gel	97. learn	146. rent	
49. gelatin	98. leg	147. rental	

#28

How many words can you make from these 9 letters? There is no letter which must be used in every word. You can use only these 9 letters and a letter cannot be used more than once in any word (you may use 2 N's). It's possible to make one 9-letter word.

Score: 20 words or more – EXCELLENT

     15 words or more – VERY GOOD

     10 words or more - GOOD

Hint: don't forget the plural forms of words, for example ace is 1 word and aces is a 2nd word. It's possible to make 151 words of 3 or more letters. (See following page for answers).

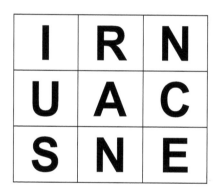

Answers:

1. ace	39. crane	77. nacre	115. sac
2. aces	40. cranes	78. nacres	116. sane
3. acne	41. crannies	79. narc	117. saner
4. acre	42. cries	80. narcs	118. sari
5. acres	43. cruise	81. near	119. sauce
6. Ainu	44. cue	82. nears	120. saucier
7. Ainus	45. cues	83. nice	121. scan
8. air	46. cur	84. nicer	122. scanner
9. airs	47. cure	85. nine	123. scar
10. anise	48. cures	86. nines	124. scare
11. anus	49. curie	87. nuance	125. sea
12. arc	50. curs	88. nuisance	126. sear
13. arcs	51. curse	89. nun	127. sec
14. are	52. ear	90. nuns	128. sic
15. Aries	53. earn	91. nurse	129. sienna
16. arise	54. earns	92. race	130. sin
17. arisen	55. ears	93. races	131. since
18. arsenic	56. ecru	94. rain	132. sine
19. cairn	57. ennui	95. rains	133. sinner
20. cairns	58. era	96. raise	134. sir
21. can	59. ice	97. ran	135. sire
22. cane	60. ices	98. rein	136. siren
23. caner	61. inane	99. reins	137. snare
24. canes	62. inaner	100. resin	138. sucre
25. canine	63. Inca	101. rice	139. sue
26. canines	64. Incas	102. rices	140. sun
27. canner	65. incur	103. rinse	141. Sunni
28. cannier	66. incurs	104. rise	142. sunnier
29. cans	67. inn	105. risen	143. sure
30. car	68. inner	106. rue	144. urea
31. care	69. inns	107. rues	145. uric
32. cares	70. ins	108. ruin	146. urine
33. caries	71. insane	109. ruins	147. urn
34. cars	72. insurance	110. run	148. urns
35. case	73. insure	111. rune	149. ursine
36. casein	74. inure	112. runes	150. use
37. cause	75. inures	113. runs	151. user
38. causer	76. ire	114. ruse	

56

#29

How many words can you make from these 9 letters? There is no letter which must be used in every word. You can use only these 9 letters and a letter cannot be used more than once in any word (you may use 2 E's). It's possible to make one 9-letter word.

Score: 20 words or more – EXCELLENT

     15 words or more – VERY GOOD

     10 words or more - GOOD

It's possible to make 123 words of 3 or more letters. (See following page for answers).

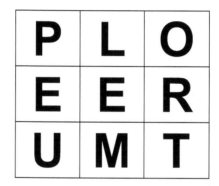

Answers:

1. eel	42. motel	83. remote
2. elm	43. mule	84. rep
3. elope	44. mute	85. repel
4. eloper	45. muter	86. repute
5. emote	46. omelet	87. roe
6. ere	47. opt	88. role
7. erupt	48. ore	89. romp
8. lee	49. our	90. rope
9. leer	50. out	91. rot
10. lemur	51. outer	92. rote
11. Leo	52. peel	93. rout
12. leper	53. peer	94. route
13. let	54. pelt	95. rue
14. letup	55. pelter	96. rule
15. lop	56. per	97. rum
16. lope	57. perm	98. rump
17. lore	58. pert	99. rumple
18. lot	59. pet	100. rupee
19. lout	60. peter	101. rut
20. lump	61. petrel	102. tee
21. lure	62. petrol	103. teem
22. lute	63. petroleum	104. temper
23. meet	64. plot	105. temple
24. melt	65. plum	106. tempo
25. melter	66. plume	107. term
26. mere	67. Pluto	108. toe
27. met	68. poem	109. tom
28. mete	69. poet	110. tome
29. meteor	70. pole	111. top
30. meter	71. pore	112. toper
31. metre	72. port	113. tore
32. mol	73. pot	114. toupee
33. mole	74. pour	115. tour
34. molt	75. pout	116. tree
35. mop	76. pouter	117. tromp
36. mope	77. pro	118. trope
37. moper	78. prom	119. troupe
38. more	79. pure	120. true
39. morel	80. purl	121. trump
40. mot	81. put	122. tumor
41. mote	82. reel	123. tupelo

#30

How many words can you make from these 9 letters? There is no letter which must be used in every word. You can use only these 9 letters and a letter cannot be used more than once in any word (you may use 2 C's). It's possible to make one 9-letter word.

Score: 20 words or more – EXCELLENT

15 words or more – VERY GOOD

10 words or more - GOOD

Hint: don't forget the plural forms of words, for example ace is 1 word and aces is a 2nd word. It's possible to make 132 words of 3 or more letters. (See following page for answers).

C	A	L
C	H	S
I	M	E

Answers:

1. ace	34. chemical	67. ices	100. mesh
2. aces	35. chemicals	68. ilea	101. mica
3. ache	36. chi	69. Islam	102. Micah
4. aches	37. chic	70. isle	103. micas
5. acme	38. chime	71. lace	104. mice
6. ahem	39. chimes	72. laces	105. mil
7. ail	40. chisel	73. lam	106. mile
8. ails	41. claim	74. lame	107. miles
9. aim	42. claims	75. lames	108. mils
10. aims	43. clam	76. lams	109. sac
11. aisle	44. clams	77. lash	110. sachem
12. alchemic	45. clash	78. lea	111. sail
13. ale	46. clime	79. leach	112. sale
14. ales	47. climes	80. leash	113. same
15. alms	48. each	81. lice	114. scale
16. Amish	49. elm	82. lie	115. scam
17. ash	50. elms	83. lies	116. schema
18. cache	51. hail	84. lime	117. sea
19. caches	52. hails	85. limes	118. seal
20. calm	53. hale	86. mace	119. seam
21. calms	54. hales	87. maces	120. sec
22. cam	55. ham	88. mach	121. semi
23. came	56. hams	89. mail	122. shale
24. camel	57. has	90. mails	123. sham
25. camels	58. heal	91. male	124. shame
26. cams	59. heals	92. males	125. she
27. case	60. helm	93. malice	126. shim
28. cash	61. helms	94. mash	127. sic
29. chaise	62. hem	95. meal	128. slam
30. chalice	63. hems	96. meals	129. slice
31. chalices	64. him	97. Mecca	130. slim
32. chase	65. his	98. mesa	131. slime
33. chasm	66. ice	99. mescal	132. smile

#31

How many words can you make from these 9 letters? There is no letter which must be used in every word. You can use only these 9 letters and a letter cannot be used more than once in any word (you may use 2 R's and 2 T's). It's possible to make one 9-letter word.

Score: 20 words or more – EXCELLENT

    15 words or more – VERY GOOD

    10 words or more - GOOD

Hint: don't forget the plural forms of words, for example ant is 1 word and ants is a 2nd word. It's possible to make 129 words of 3 or more letters. (See following page for answers).

T	A	R
N	P	S
O	T	R

Answers:

1. ant	34. pat	67. snap	100. taros
2. ants	35. patron	68. snort	101. tarot
3. apron	36. patrons	69. snot	102. tarots
4. aprons	37. pats	70. soap	103. tarp
5. apt	38. porn	71. soar	104. tarpon
6. arson	39. port	72. son	105. tarpons
7. art	40. ports	73. sonar	106. tarps
8. arts	41. post	74. sop	107. tars
9. asp	42. pot	75. sort	108. tart
10. atop	43. pots	76. sot	109. tarts
11. nap	44. pro	77. spa	110. tat
12. naps	45. pros	78. span	111. tats
13. nor	46. ran	79. spar	112. toast
14. not	47. rant	80. spat	113. ton
15. oar	48. rants	81. sporran	114. tons
16. oars	49. rap	82. sport	115. top
17. oat	50. raps	83. spot	116. tops
18. oats	51. rapt	84. sprat	117. tor
19. opt	52. raptor	85. star	118. torn
20. opts	53. raptors	86. start	119. tors
21. pan	54. rasp	87. stat	120. tort
22. pans	55. rat	88. stoat	121. torts
23. pant	56. rats	89. stop	122. tot
24. pants	57. roan	90. strap	123. tots
25. par	58. roans	91. strop	124. transport
26. parrot	59. roar	92. tan	125. trap
27. parrots	60. roars	93. tans	126. traps
28. pars	61. roast	94. tap	127. trot
29. parson	62. rostra	95. taps	128. trots
30. part	63. rot	96. tar	129. tsar
31. parts	64. rots	97. tarn	
32. past	65. sap	98. tarns	
33. pastor	66. sat	99. taro	

#32

How many words can you make from these 9 letters? There is no letter which must be used in every word. You can use only these 9 letters and a letter cannot be used more than once in any word. It's possible to make one 9-letter word.

Score: 20 words or more – EXCELLENT
    15 words or more – VERY GOOD
    10 words or more - GOOD

It's possible to make 152 words of 3 or more letters. (See following page for answers).

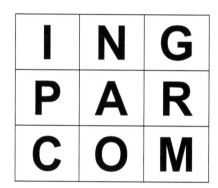

Answers:

1. acing	40. con	79. mango	118. pica
2. acorn	41. cop	80. manic	119. pig
3. ago	42. coping	81. manioc	120. pin
4. aim	43. copra	82. manor	121. ping
5. air	44. coring	83. Maori	122. poi
6. amigo	45. corm	84. map	123. poring
7. amir	46. corn	85. mar	124. porn
8. among	47. crag	86. margin	125. pram
9. amp	48. cram	87. mica	126. prig
10. aping	49. cramp	88. micra	127. prim
11. apron	50. cramping	89. micro	128. prion
12. arc	51. crampon	90. micron	129. pro
13. arcing	52. crimp	91. min	130. prom
14. argon	53. crop	92. mina	131. prong
15. arm	54. gain	93. minor	132. racing
16. arming	55. gamin	94. moan	133. rag
17. cairn	56. gap	95. mop	134. rain
18. cam	57. gar	96. moping	135. ram
19. camp	58. gimp	97. morn	136. ramp
20. camping	59. gin	98. nag	137. ramping
21. can	60. grain	99. nap	138. ran
22. cap	61. gram	100. narc	139. rang
23. capo	62. grim	101. nip	140. rap
24. capon	63. grin	102. nor	141. raping
25. car	64. grip	103. norm	142. rig
26. cargo	65. groan	104. oar	143. rim
27. caring	66. groin	105. oaring	144. ring
28. carom	67. icon	106. orca	145. rip
29. caroming	68. imago	107. organ	146. roam
30. carp	69. imp	108. organic	147. roaming
31. carping	70. Inca	109. pacing	148. roan
32. ciao	71. ion	110. pain	149. Roman
33. cigar	72. iron	111. pair	150. romp
34. cir	73. macro	112. pan	151. romping
35. cog	74. macron	113. pang	152. roping
36. coin	75. magi	114. panic	
37. coma	76. magic	115. par	
38. coming	77. main	116. paring	
39. comparing	78. man	117. piano	

#33

How many words can you make from these 9 letters? Every word must contain the letter "E". You can use only these 9 letters and a letter cannot be used more than once in any word. It's possible to make one 9-letter word.

Score: 20 words or more – EXCELLENT

    15 words or more – VERY GOOD

    10 words or more - GOOD

Hint: don't forget the plural forms of words, for example age is 1 word and ages is a 2nd word. It's possible to make 192 words of 3 or more letters. (See following page for answers).

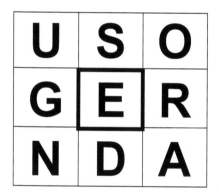

Answers:

1. adore	49. drogue	97. Negro	145. rouse
2. adores	50. drogues	98. nerd	146. roused
3. aeon	51. drone	99. nerds	147. rude
4. aeons	52. drones	100. node	148. rue
5. age	53. due	101. nodes	149. rued
6. aged	54. dues	102. Norse	150. rues
7. ager	55. dune	103. nose	151. rune
8. ages	56. ear	104. nosed	152. runes
9. ague	57. earn	105. nude	153. ruse
10. agues	58. earns	106. nudge	154. sage
11. anger	59. ears	107. nudges	155. sager
12. angers	60. ego	108. nurse	156. sander
13. anode	61. egos	109. nursed	157. sane
14. anodes	62. end	110. oared	158. saner
15. are	63. ends	111. ode	159. sea
16. Ares	64. enduro	112. odes	160. sear
17. argue	65. eon	113. ogre	161. sedan
18. argued	66. era	114. ogres	162. send
19. argues	67. erg	115. one	163. sera
20. arose	68. ergo	116. ones	164. snare
21. arouse	69. ergs	117. orange	165. snared
22. aroused	70. eros	118. ore	166. snore
23. asunder	71. gander	119. Osage	167. snored
24. auger	72. ganders	120. rage	168. soared
25. augers	73. garden	121. raged	169. sore
26. Dane	74. gardens	122. rages	170. sounder
27. Danes	75. gear	123. range	171. soured
28. danger	76. gears	124. ranged	172. sue
29. dangerous	77. genus	125. ranges	173. sued
30. dangers	78. gerund	126. rase	174. sugared
31. dare	79. gerunds	127. rased	175. sundae
32. dares	80. goes	128. read	176. sunder
33. dean	81. gone	129. reads	177. sure
34. deans	82. goner	130. reason	178. surge
35. dear	83. gore	131. red	179. surged
36. dears	84. gored	132. reds	180. surgeon
37. den	85. gores	133. rend	181. under
38. dens	86. gorse	134. rends	182. undergo
39. doe	87. gourde	135. resound	183. undoes
40. doer	88. grade	136. rode	184. unread
41. doers	89. grades	137. roe	185. urea
42. does	90. groaned	138. roes	186. urge
43. doge	91. grouse	139. rogue	187. urged
44. doges	92. groused	140. rogues	188. urges
45. done	93. nae	141. rose	189. usage
46. dose	94. nares	142. rouge	190. use
47. douse	95. near	143. rouged	191. used
48. douser	96. nears	144. rouges	192. user

#34

How many words can you make from these 9 letters? Every word must contain the letter "A". You can use only these 9 letters and a letter cannot be used more than once in any word (you may use 2 A's). It's possible to make one 9-letter word.

Score: 20 words or more – EXCELLENT

15 words or more – VERY GOOD

10 words or more - GOOD

Hint: don't forget the plural forms of words, for example mat is 1 word and mats is a 2nd word. It's possible to make 210 words of 3 or more letters. (See following page for answers).

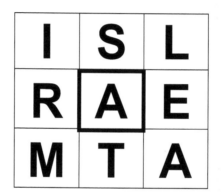

Answers:

1. aerial	54. earls	107. mate	160. slat
2. ail	55. ears	108. material	161. slate
3. ails	56. east	109. materials	162. smart
4. aim	57. eat	110. mates	163. smear
5. aims	58. eats	111. mats	164. stair
6. air	59. era	112. meal	165. stale
7. airs	60. ilea	113. meals	166. staler
8. aisle	61. irate	114. meat	167. star
9. ala	62. Islam	115. mesa	168. stare
10. alarm	63. Israel	116. metal	169. steal
11. alarmist	64. lair	117. metals	170. steam
12. alarms	65. lairs	118. rail	171. stream
13. alas	66. lam	119. rails	172. stria
14. ale	67. lama	120. raise	173. striae
15. alert	68. Lamaist	121. ram	174. Tai
16. alerts	69. lamas	122. Rama	175. tail
17. ales	70. lame	123. ramie	176. tails
18. alias	71. lamer	124. rams	177. Tais
19. alit	72. lames	125. rat	178. tala
20. alms	73. lamest	126. rate	179. talas
21. altar	74. lams	127. rates	180. tale
22. altars	75. lariat	128. rats	181. tales
23. alter	76. lariats	129. real	182. tali
24. alters	77. laser	130. realism	183. tamale
25. amir	78. last	131. realist	184. tamales
26. amirs	79. late	132. realm	185. tame
27. are	80. later	133. realms	186. tamer
28. area	81. lea	134. reals	187. tames
29. areas	82. least	135. ream	188. Tamil
30. Ares	83. liar	136. reams	189. Tamils
31. aria	84. liars	137. retail	190. tar
32. arias	85. lira	138. retails	191. tare
33. Aries	86. mail	139. rial	192. tares
34. aril	87. mails	140. rials	193. tars
35. arils	88. malaise	141. sail	194. tarsal
36. arise	89. male	142. salami	195. tarsi
37. arm	90. males	143. sale	196. tea
38. armies	91. malt	144. salt	197. teal
39. armlet	92. malts	145. saltier	198. teals
40. armlets	93. mar	146. same	199. team
41. arms	94. mare	147. sari	200. teams
42. art	95. mares	148. sat	201. tear
43. Artemis	96. marital	149. sate	202. tears
44. arts	97. marl	150. satire	203. teas
45. aster	98. marls	151. sea	204. tiara
46. astir	99. mars	152. seal	205. trail
47. astral	100. mart	153. seam	206. trails
48. ate	101. martial	154. sear	207. tram
49. atlas	102. marts	155. seat	208. trams
50. atria	103. maser	156. sera	209. trial
51. atrial	104. mast	157. serial	210. tsar
52. ear	105. master	158. sitar	
53. earl	106. mat	159. slam	

#35

How many words can you make from these 9 letters?
There is no letter which must be used in every word.
You can use only these 9 letters and a letter cannot be
used more than once in any word (you may use 2 E's
and 2 F's). It's possible to make one 9-letter word.
Score: 20 words or more – EXCELLENT
    15 words or more – VERY GOOD
    10 words or more - GOOD
It's possible to make 121 words of 3 or more letters.
(See following page for answers).

D	N	R
I	E	T
F	E	F

Answers:

1. deer
2. defer
3. defier
4. define
5. definer
6. deft
7. defter
8. den
9. denier
10. dent
11. deter
12. die
13. diet
14. dieter
15. differ
16. different
17. din
18. dine
19. diner
20. dint
21. dire
22. dirt
23. drift
24. Eden
25. edit
26. eft
27. eider
28. end
29. enter
30. entire
31. ere
32. Erie
33. fed
34. fee
35. feed
36. feet
37. feint
38. feinted
39. fen
40. fend
41. fender
42. fern
43. fete
44. feted
45. fetid
46. fie
47. fief
48. fiend
49. fife
50. fifer
51. fifteen
52. fin
53. find
54. finder
55. fine
56. fined
57. finer
58. fir
59. fire
60. fired
61. fit
62. free
63. freed
64. fret
65. fried
66. friend
67. inert
68. infer
69. inter
70. ire
71. nee
72. need
73. nerd
74. net
75. nit
76. niter
77. nitre
78. red
79. reed
80. reef
81. refine
82. refined
83. rein
84. reined
85. rend
86. rent
87. rented
88. rid
89. ride
90. rife
91. riff
92. riffed
93. rift
94. rifted
95. rind
96. rite
97. tee
98. teed
99. teen
100. ten
101. tend
102. tender
103. tern
104. tide
105. tie
106. tied
107. tier
108. tiered
109. tiff
110. tiffed
111. tin
112. tinder
113. tine
114. tined
115. tire
116. tired
117. tree
118. treed
119. trend
120. tried
121. trine

#36

How many words can you make from these 9 letters? Every word must contain the letter "E". You can use only these 9 letters and a letter cannot be used more than once in any word (you may use 2 L's). It's possible to make one 9-letter word.

Score: 20 words or more – EXCELLENT

    15 words or more – VERY GOOD

    10 words or more - GOOD

Hint: don't forget the plural forms of words, for example ear is 1 word and ears is a 2nd word. It's possible to make 170 words of 3 or more letters. (See following page for answers).

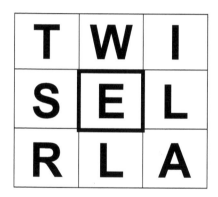

Answers:

1. aisle	44. lire	87. site	130. tires
2. ale	45. lisle	88. slate	131. trellis
3. alert	46. liter	89. slew	132. tries
4. alerts	47. literal	90. slier	133. wailer
5. ales	48. literals	91. stairwell	134. waiter
6. allies	49. liters	92. stale	135. waiters
7. alter	50. litre	93. staler	136. wale
8. alters	51. litres	94. stare	137. wales
9. are	52. lwei	95. steal	138. wallet
10. Aries	53. raise	96. stellar	139. wallets
11. arise	54. rallies	97. stew	140. ware
12. aster	55. rase	98. stile	141. wares
13. ate	56. rate	99. stiller	142. wariest
14. awe	57. rates	100. strew	143. waste
15. awes	58. rawest	101. striae	144. waster
16. ear	59. real	102. swear	145. wastrel
17. earl	60. realist	103. sweat	146. water
18. earls	61. reals	104. swell	147. waters
19. ears	62. reis	105. tale	148. weal
20. east	63. rest	106. tales	149. wear
21. eat	64. retail	107. taller	150. wears
22. eats	65. retails	108. tallies	151. weir
23. ell	66. riel	109. tare	152. weirs
24. ells	67. riels	110. tares	153. well
25. era	68. rile	111. tea	154. wells
26. ilea	69. riles	112. teal	155. welt
27. irate	70. rise	113. teals	156. welts
28. ire	71. rite	114. tear	157. wert
29. isle	72. rites	115. tears	158. west
30. islet	73. sale	116. teas	159. wet
31. Israel	74. saltier	117. tell	160. wets
32. laser	75. sate	118. tells	161. wile
33. late	76. satire	119. tie	162. wiles
34. later	77. sea	120. tier	163. wire
35. lea	78. seal	121. tiers	164. wires
36. least	79. sear	122. ties	165. wise
37. lei	80. seat	123. tile	166. wiser
38. leis	81. sell	124. tiler	167. wrest
39. lest	82. sera	125. tilers	168. wriest
40. let	83. serial	126. tiles	169. write
41. lets	84. set	127. tiller	170. writes
42. lie	85. sew	128. tillers	
43. lies	86. sire	129. tire	

#37

How many words can you make from these 9 letters? There is no letter which must be used in every word. You can use only these 9 letters and a letter cannot be used more than once in any word. It's possible to make one 9-letter word.

Score: 20 words or more – EXCELLENT

    15 words or more – VERY GOOD

    10 words or more - GOOD

It's possible to make 124 words of 3 or more letters. (See following page for answers).

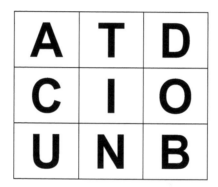

A	T	D
C	I	O
U	N	B

Answers: _____ _____ _____

_____ _____ _____ _____

_____ _____ _____ _____

_____ _____ _____ _____

_____ _____ _____ _____

_____ _____ _____ _____

_____ _____ _____ _____

_____ _____ _____ _____

_____ _____ _____ _____

_____ _____ _____ _____

_____ _____ _____ _____

_____ _____ _____ _____

_____ _____ _____ _____

_____ _____ _____ _____

1. abduct
2. abduction
3. abound
4. about
5. abut
6. acid
7. act
8. actin
9. action
10. ado
11. aid
12. Ainu
13. and
14. ant
15. antic
16. auction
17. audio
18. audit
19. aunt
20. auto
21. bacon
22. bad
23. bait
24. ban
25. band
26. bandit
27. Bantu
28. bat
29. baton
30. baud
31. bid
32. bin
33. bind
34. biota
35. bit
36. boa
37. boat
38. bond
39. bound
40. bout
41. bud
42. bun
43. bunt
44. but
45. cab
46. cabin
47. cad
48. can
49. cant
50. canto
51. cat
52. caution
53. ciao
54. coat
55. coati
56. cob
57. cod
58. coda
59. coin
60. con
61. conduit
62. cot
63. count
64. cub
65. cubit
66. cud
67. cut
68. dab
69. daub
70. daunt
71. dicot
72. dicta
73. din
74. dint
75. don
76. donut
77. dot
78. doubt
79. dub
80. ducat
81. duct
82. dun
83. duo
84. Ibo
85. icon
86. Inca
87. induct
88. into
89. ion
90. iota
91. nab
92. nib
93. nit
94. nod
95. not
96. nub
97. nut
98. oat
99. obi
100. obit
101. obtain
102. Odin
103. out
104. outbid
105. tab
106. taco
107. tad
108. Tai
109. Taino
110. tan
111. tau
112. tic
113. tin
114. toad
115. ton
116. tonic
117. toucan
118. tub
119. tuba
120. tuna
121. tunic
122. undo
123. unit
124. unto

#38

How many words can you make from these 9 letters? There is no letter which must be used in every word. You can use only these 9 letters and a letter cannot be used more than once in any word (you may use 2 B's and 2 E's). It's possible to make one 9-letter word.

Score: 20 words or more – EXCELLENT

    15 words or more – VERY GOOD

    10 words or more - GOOD

It's possible to make 98 words of 3 or more letters. (See following page for answers).

B	C	B
D	E	U
R	E	A

Answers:

1. abed
2. ace
3. aced
4. acerb
5. acre
6. arc
7. arced
8. are
9. babe
10. bad
11. bade
12. bar
13. barb
14. barbecue
15. <u>barbecued</u>
16. barbed
17. bard
18. bare
19. bared
20. baud
21. bead
22. bear
23. beard
24. beau
25. bed
26. bedaub
27. bee
28. beer
29. bra
30. brace
31. braced
32. brad
33. bread
34. bred
35. breed
36. bud
37. bur
38. cab
39. cad
40. cadre
41. car
42. card
43. care
44. cared
45. cedar
46. cede
47. crab
48. crabbed
49. Cree
50. creed
51. crude
52. cub
53. cube
54. cubed
55. cud
56. cue
57. cued
58. cur
59. curb
60. curbed
61. curd
62. cure
63. cured
64. dab
65. dace
66. dare
67. daub
68. dauber
69. dear
70. debar
71. deer
72. deuce
73. drab
74. drub
75. dub
76. due
77. ear
78. eared
79. ebb
80. ebbed
81. ecru
82. educe
83. era
84. ere
85. race
86. raced
87. rad
88. read
89. red
90. reduce
91. reed
92. rub
93. rubbed
94. rube
95. rude
96. rue
97. rued
98. urea

#39

How many words can you make from these 9 letters? There is no letter which must be used in every word. You can use only these 9 letters and a letter cannot be used more than once in any word (you may use 2 L's). It's possible to make one 9-letter word.

Score: 20 words or more – EXCELLENT

15 words or more – VERY GOOD

10 words or more - GOOD

Hint: don't forget the plural forms of words, for example ball is 1 word and balls is a 2nd word. It's possible to make 152 words of 3 or more letters. (See following page for answers).

L	S	L
E	A	H
U	D	B

Answers:

1. abed	39. blue	77. ell	115. lads
2. able	40. blued	78. ells	116. lash
3. abuse	41. blues	79. had	117. lashed
4. abused	42. blush	80. Hades	118. laud
5. ads	43. blushed	81. hale	119. lauds
6. alb	44. bud	82. haled	120. lea
7. albs	45. buds	83. hales	121. lead
8. ale	46. bull	84. hall	122. leads
9. ales	47. bulled	85. halls	123. leash
10. all	48. bullhead	86. has	124. led
11. allude	49. bullheads	87. haul	125. lube
12. alludes	50. bulls	88. hauled	126. lubed
13. ash	51. bus	89. hauls	127. lubes
14. bad	52. bused	90. head	128. lush
15. bade	53. bush	91. heads	129. sable
16. bald	54. bushed	92. heal	130. sad
17. bale	55. bushel	93. heals	131. sale
18. baled	56. dab	94. held	132. sea
19. bales	57. dabs	95. hell	133. seal
20. ball	58. dale	96. hells	134. sell
21. balled	59. dales	97. hub	135. shad
22. balls	60. dash	98. hubs	136. shade
23. base	61. daub	99. hue	137. shale
24. based	62. daubs	100. hues	138. shall
25. bash	63. deal	101. hula	139. she
26. bashed	64. deals	102. hulas	140. shed
27. baud	65. debs	103. hull	141. shell
28. bead	66. dell	104. hulled	142. slab
29. beads	67. dells	105. hulls	143. sled
30. beau	68. dual	106. lab	144. slue
31. beaus	69. dub	107. label	145. slued
32. bed	70. dubs	108. labels	146. sub
33. beds	71. due	109. labs	147. subhead
34. bell	72. duel	110. lad	148. sue
35. bells	73. duels	111. lade	149. sued
36. blade	74. dues	112. lades	150. usable
37. blades	75. dull	113. ladle	151. use
38. bled	76. dulls	114. ladles	152. used

#40

How many words can you make from these 9 letters? There is no letter which must be used in every word. You can use only these 9 letters and a letter cannot be used more than once in any word. It's possible to make one 9-letter word.

Score: 20 words or more – EXCELLENT

    15 words or more – VERY GOOD

    10 words or more - GOOD

Hint: don't forget the plural forms of words, for example hen is 1 word and hens is a 2nd word. It's possible to make 166 words of 3 or more letters. (See following page for answers).

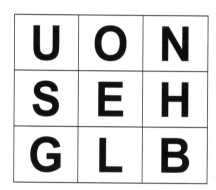

Answers:

1. beg	43. egos	85. hubs	127. nobles
2. begs	44. enough	86. hue	128. noel
3. begun	45. eon	87. hues	129. noes
4. belong	46. gel	88. hug	130. nose
5. belongs	47. gels	89. huge	131. nosh
6. blouse	48. genus	90. hugs	132. nub
7. blue	49. ghoul	91. Hun	133. nubs
8. blues	50. ghouls	92. hung	134. ogle
9. blush	51. glen	93. Huns	135. ogles
10. bog	52. glens	94. leg	136. one
11. bogs	53. glob	95. legs	137. ones
12. bogus	54. globe	96. lens	138. onus
13. bole	55. globes	97. Leo	139. sen
14. boles	56. globs	98. lob	140. she
15. bolus	57. glue	99. lobe	141. shoe
16. bone	58. glues	100. lobes	142. shogun
17. bones	59. gluon	101. lobs	143. shone
18. bong	60. gluons	102. log	144. shun
19. bongs	61. gnu	103. loge	145. slob
20. bonus	62. gob	104. loges	146. sloe
21. bosh	63. gobs	105. logs	147. slog
22. bosun	64. goes	106. lone	148. slough
23. bough	65. gone	107. long	149. slue
24. boughs	66. gosh	108. longs	150. slug
25. bug	67. gun	109. lose	151. slung
26. bugle	68. guns	110. lounge	152. snob
27. bugles	69. gush	111. lounges	153. snub
28. bugs	70. hen	112. louse	154. snug
29. bulge	71. hens	113. lube	155. sob
30. bulges	72. hob	114. lubes	156. sol
31. bun	73. hobs	115. lug	157. sole
32. bung	74. hoe	116. luge	158. son
33. bunghole	75. hoes	117. luges	159. song
34. bungholes	76. hog	118. lugs	160. sough
35. bungle	77. hogs	119. lung	161. soul
36. bungles	78. hole	120. lunge	162. sub
37. bungs	79. holes	121. lunges	163. sue
38. buns	80. hone	122. lungs	164. sun
39. bus	81. hones	123. lush	165. sung
40. bush	82. hose	124. neb	166. use
41. bushel	83. house	125. nebs	
42. ego	84. hub	126. noble	

bung·hole (bŭng/hōl′) *n.* The hole in a cask, keg, or barrel through which liquid is poured in or drained out.

#41

How many words can you make from these 9 letters? There is no letter which must be used in every word. You can use only these 9 letters and a letter cannot be used more than once in any word (you may use 2 C's). It's possible to make one 9-letter word.

Score: 20 words or more – EXCELLENT

    15 words or more – VERY GOOD

    10 words or more - GOOD

It's possible to make 109 words of 3 or more letters. (See following page for answers).

A	R	C
E	O	R
M	D	C

Answers:

1. accord
2. ace
3. aced
4. acme
5. acre
6. ado
7. adore
8. adorer
9. arc
10. arced
11. ardor
12. are
13. arm
14. armed
15. armor
16. armored
17. cad
18. cadre
19. cam
20. camcorder
21. came
22. cameo
23. car
24. card
25. carder
26. care
27. cared
28. carom
29. caromed
30. cedar
31. cero
32. coca
33. cod
34. coda
35. code
36. coed
37. coma

38. come
39. comer
40. comrade
41. cord
42. core
43. cored
44. corm
45. cram
46. cream
47. credo
48. dace
49. dam
50. dame
51. dare
52. darer
53. dear
54. decor
55. demo
56. derma
57. doe
58. doer
59. dome
60. dorm
61. dormer
62. Draco
63. dram
64. dream
65. drear
66. ear
67. Edam
68. era
69. err
70. mace
71. macro
72. mad
73. made
74. mar

75. mare
76. marred
77. mead
78. mecca
79. mod
80. mode
81. more
82. oar
83. oared
84. ode
85. orca
86. order
87. ore
88. race
89. raced
90. racer
91. rad
92. ram
93. ramrod
94. rare
95. read
96. ream
97. rear
98. record
99. red
100. remora
101. road
102. roam
103. roamed
104. roamer
105. roar
106. roared
107. rod
108. rode
109. roe

#42

How many words can you make from these 9 letters? There is no letter which must be used in every word. You can use only these 9 letters and a letter cannot be used more than once in any word (you may use 2 A's, 2 T's and 2 S's). It's possible to make one 9-letter word.

Score: 20 words or more – EXCELLENT

    15 words or more – VERY GOOD

    10 words or more - GOOD

Hint: don't forget the plural forms of words, for example ace is 1 word and aces is a 2nd word. It's possible to make 101 words of 3 or more letters. (See following page for answers).

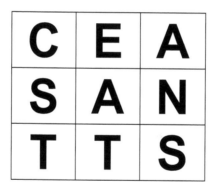

Answers:

1. ace
2. aces
3. acne
4. act
5. acts
6. ant
7. ante
8. antes
9. ants
10. Asante
11. ascent
12. ascents
13. ass
14. assent
15. asset
16. ate
17. can
18. cane
19. canes
20. cans
21. canst
22. cant
23. cants
24. case
25. cases
26. cast
27. castanet
28. castanets
29. caste
30. castes
31. casts
32. cat
33. cats
34. cent
35. cents
36. east
37. eat
38. eats
39. enact
40. enacts
41. nae
42. neat
43. nest
44. nests
45. net
46. nets
47. sac
48. sacs
49. sancta
50. sane
51. sanest
52. sans
53. sat
54. Satan
55. sate
56. sates
57. scan
58. scans
59. scant
60. scantest
61. scants
62. scat
63. scats
64. scent
65. scents
66. sea
67. seas
68. seat
69. seats
70. sec
71. secant
72. sect
73. sects
74. sen
75. sent
76. set
77. sets
78. stance
79. stances
80. stat
81. state
82. states
83. stats
84. stet
85. stets
86. tact
87. tan
88. tans
89. taste
90. tastes
91. tat
92. tea
93. teas
94. teat
95. ten
96. tens
97. tent
98. tents
99. test
100. tests
101. Tet

#43

How many words can you make from these 9 letters? There is no letter which must be used in every word. You can use only these 9 letters and a letter cannot be used more than once in any word (you may use 2 A's). It's possible to make one 9-letter word.

Score: 20 words or more – EXCELLENT

   15 words or more – VERY GOOD

   10 words or more - GOOD

Hint: don't forget the plural forms of words, for example ace is 1 word and aces is a 2nd word. It's possible to make 124 words of 3 or more letters. (See following page for answers).

A	K	M
L	E	S
A	B	C

Answers: ___ ___ ___ ___

1. aback	43. black	85. lama
2. abase	44. blacks	86. lamas
3. abeam	45. blame	87. lamb
4. able	46. blames	88. lambs
5. ace	47. bleak	89. lame
6. aces	48. cab	90. lames
7. acme	49. cabal	91. lams
8. ala	50. cabals	92. lea
9. alas	51. cable	93. leak
10. alb	52. cables	94. leaks
11. albs	53. cabs	95. mace
12. ale	54. cake	96. maces
13. ales	55. cakes	97. make
14. alms	56. calk	98. makes
15. amble	57. calks	99. male
16. ambles	58. calm	100. males
17. ameba	59. calms	101. mask
18. amebas	60. cam	102. maskable
19. ask	61. came	103. meal
20. Baal	62. camel	104. meals
21. back	63. camels	105. mesa
22. backs	64. cams	106. mescal
23. bake	65. case	107. sable
24. bakes	66. cask	108. sac
25. bale	67. clam	109. sack
26. bales	68. clambake	110. sake
27. balk	69. clambakes	111. sale
28. balks	70. clams	112. samba
29. balm	71. elk	113. same
30. balms	72. elks	114. scab
31. balsa	73. elm	115. scale
32. balsam	74. elms	116. scam
33. basal	75. kale	117. sea
34. base	76. lab	118. seal
35. bask	77. labs	119. seam
36. beak	78. lace	120. slab
37. beaks	79. laces	121. slack
38. beam	80. lack	122. slake
39. beams	81. lacks	123. slam
40. becalm	82. lake	124. smack
41. becalms	83. lakes	
42. beck	84. lam	

#44

How many words can you make from these 9 letters? There is no letter which must be used in every word. You can use only these 9 letters and a letter cannot be used more than once in any word (you may use 2 E's). It's possible to make one 9-letter word.

Score: 20 words or more – EXCELLENT

    15 words or more – VERY GOOD

    10 words or more - GOOD

It's possible to make 114 words of 3 or more letters. (See following page for answers).

M	A	E
H	I	C
P	D	E

Answers:

1. ace	39. dace	77. idem
2. aced	40. Dai	78. imp
3. ache	41. dam	79. impeach
4. ached	42. dame	80. impeached
5. acid	43. damp	81. imped
6. acme	44. decamp	82. impede
7. ahem	45. deem	83. mace
8. aid	46. deep	84. mach
9. aide	47. deice	85. mad
10. aim	48. dice	86. made
11. aimed	49. die	87. Mahdi
12. amid	50. dim	88. maid
13. amp	51. dime	89. map
14. ape	52. dip	90. mead
15. aped	53. each	91. Mede
16. aphid	54. Edam	92. Medea
17. apiece	55. edema	93. media
18. cad	56. epic	94. medic
19. cam	57. had	95. meed
20. came	58. ham	96. mica
21. camp	59. hap	97. Micah
22. camped	60. head	98. mice
23. cap	61. heap	99. mid
24. cape	62. heaped	100. pace
25. cede	63. heed	101. paced
26. cedi	64. hem	102. pad
27. champ	65. heme	103. paid
28. champed	66. hemp	104. pea
29. chap	67. hep	105. peace
30. cheap	68. hid	106. peach
31. cheep	69. hide	107. peached
32. chi	70. hie	108. phi
33. chid	71. hied	109. pica
34. chide	72. him	110. pie
35. chime	73. hip	111. piece
36. chimed	74. ice	112. pieced
37. chimp	75. iced	113. pied
38. chip	76. idea	114. Pima

#45

How many words can you make from these 9 letters? Every word must contain the letter "E". You can only use these 9 letters and a letter cannot be used more than once in any word. It's possible to make one 9-letter word.

Score: 20 words or more – EXCELLENT

15 words or more – VERY GOOD

10 words or more - GOOD

Hint: don't forget the plural forms of words, for example ace is 1 word and aces is a 2nd word. It's possible to make 136 words of 3 or more letters. (See following page for answers).

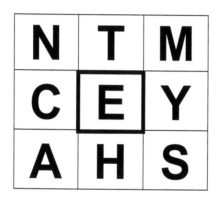

Answers:

1. ace	35. east	69. meant	103. stamen
2. aces	36. easy	70. meat	104. stance
3. ache	37. eat	71. men	105. steam
4. aches	38. eats	72. mesa	106. steamy
5. acme	39. enact	73. mesh	107. stem
6. acne	40. enacts	74. met	108. stench
7. ahem	41. encyst	75. nae	109. stye
8. amen	42. etch	76. name	110. tame
9. amnesty	43. haste	77. names	111. tames
10. ante	44. hasten	78. neat	112. tea
11. antes	45. hate	79. neath	113. teach
12. anthem	46. hates	80. nest	114. team
13. anthems	47. heat	81. net	115. teams
14. ascent	48. heats	82. nets	116. teas
15. ashen	49. hem	83. sachem	117. ten
16. ate	50. hems	84. sachet	118. tens
17. aye	51. hen	85. same	119. thane
18. ayes	52. hens	86. sane	120. thanes
19. came	53. hey	87. sate	121. the
20. cane	54. hyena	88. scent	122. them
21. canes	55. hyenas	89. schema	123. then
22. case	56. hymen	90. scythe	124. they
23. caste	57. hymens	91. sea	125. thyme
24. cent	58. mace	92. seam	126. yachtsmen
25. cents	59. maces	93. seamy	127. yea
26. chantey	60. mane	94. seat	128. yeah
27. chanteys	61. manes	95. secant	129. yeas
28. chase	62. manse	96. sect	130. yeast
29. chaste	63. mantes	97. sen	131. yen
30. chasten	64. matches	98. sent	132. yens
31. cheat	65. mate	99. set	133. yenta
32. cheats	66. mates	100. shame	134. yentas
33. chest	67. mean	101. shantey	135. yes
34. each	68. means	102. she	136. yet

#46

How many words can you make from these 9 letters? There is no letter which must be used in every word. You can use only these 9 letters and a letter cannot be used more than once in any word (you may use 2 R's). It's possible to make one 9-letter word.

Score: 20 words or more – EXCELLENT
15 words or more – VERY GOOD
10 words or more - GOOD

Hint: don't forget the plural forms of words, for example age is 1 word and ages is a 2nd word. It's possible to make 179 words of 3 or more letters. (See following page for answers).

L	S	R
W	A	R
G	E	N

Answers:

1. age	46. gears	91. rag	136. snarer
2. ager	47. gel	92. rage	137. snarl
3. ages	48. gels	93. rages	138. snarler
4. ale	49. glans	94. rags	139. swag
5. ales	50. glare	95. ran	140. swage
6. anew	51. glares	96. rang	141. swan
7. angel	52. glean	97. range	142. swear
8. angels	53. gleans	98. ranger	143. wag
9. anger	54. glen	99. rangers	144. wage
10. angers	55. glens	100. ranges	145. wager
11. angle	56. gnarl	101. rare	146. wagers
12. angles	57. gnarls	102. rase	147. wages
13. answer	58. gnaw	103. raw	148. wags
14. are	59. gnawer	104. rawer	149. wale
15. Ares	60. gnaws	105. real	150. wales
16. awe	61. grew	106. reals	151. wan
17. awes	62. lag	107. rear	152. wane
18. awl	63. lager	108. rears	153. wanes
19. awls	64. lagers	109. regal	154. wangle
20. awn	65. lags	110. renal	155. wangler
21. awns	66. lane	111. reran	156. wangles
22. ear	67. lanes	112. sag	157. wans
23. earl	68. large	113. sage	158. war
24. earls	69. larger	114. sager	159. ware
25. earn	70. laser	115. sal	160. wares
26. earns	71. law	116. sale	161. warn
27. ears	72. lawn	117. sane	162. warner
28. ens	73. lawns	118. saner	163. warns
29. era	74. laws	119. sang	164. warren
30. erg	75. lea	120. saw	165. wars
31. ergs	76. lean	121. sawer	166. was
32. err	77. leans	122. sawn	167. weal
33. errs	78. learn	123. sea	168. wean
34. Gael	79. learns	124. seal	169. weans
35. Gaels	80. leg	125. sear	170. wear
36. gal	81. legs	126. sen	171. wears
37. gale	82. lens	127. sera	172. wen
38. gales	83. nae	128. sew	173. wens
39. gals	84. nag	129. sewn	174. wrangle
40. gar	85. nags	130. slag	175. wrangler
41. garner	86. nares	131. slang	176. wranglers
42. garners	87. near	132. slaw	177. wrangles
43. gars	88. nears	133. slew	178. wren
44. gas	89. new	134. snag	179. wrens
45. gear	90. news	135. snare	

#47

How many words can you make from these 9 letters? There is no letter which must be used in every word. You can use only these 9 letters and a letter cannot be used more than once in any word (you may use 2 S's). It's possible to make one 9-letter word.

Score: 20 words or more – EXCELLENT

   15 words or more – VERY GOOD

   10 words or more - GOOD

Hint: don't forget the plural forms of words, for example age is 1 word and ages is a 2nd word. It's possible to make 212 words of 3 or more letters. (See following page for answers).

A	N	S
G	E	W
I	S	L

Answers:

93

1. aegis	44. gas	87. lie	130. sign	173. swigs
2. age	45. gases	88. lien	131. signal	174. swine
3. ages	46. gel	89. lies	132. signals	175. swing
4. agile	47. gels	90. linage	133. signs	176. swings
5. ail	48. genial	91. line	134. silage	177. wag
6. ails	49. gin	92. lines	135. sin	178. wage
7. aisle	50. gins	93. lwei	136. sine	179. wages
8. aisles	51. glans	94. nae	137. sinew	180. wags
9. ale	52. glass	95. nag	138. sinews	181. wail
10. ales	53. glean	96. nags	139. sing	182. wails
11. alien	54. gleans	97. nail	140. singe	183. wain
12. aliens	55. glen	98. nails	141. singes	184. wains
13. align	56. glens	99. new	142. single	185. wale
14. aligns	57. gnaw	100. news	143. singles	186. wales
15. aline	58. gnaws	101. nil	144. sings	187. waling
16. alines	59. gneiss	102. sag	145. sins	188. wan
17. anew	60. ilea	103. sage	146. sis	189. wane
18. angel	61. ins	104. sages	147. sisal	190. wanes
19. angels	62. isle	105. sags	148. slag	191. wangle
20. angle	63. isles	106. sail	149. slags	192. wangles
21. angles	64. lag	107. sails	150. slain	193. wans
22. anise	65. lags	108. sal	151. slang	194. was
23. anises	66. lain	109. sale	152. slangs	195. weal
24. ass	67. lane	110. sales	153. slaw	196. wean
25. assign	68. lanes	111. saline	154. slaws	197. weans
26. awe	69. lass	112. sane	155. slew	198. wen
27. awes	70. lassie	113. sang	156. slewing	199. wens
28. awing	71. law	114. sans	157. slews	200. wig
29. awl	72. lawn	115. saw	158. sling	201. wigs
30. awls	73. lawns	116. sawing	159. slings	202. wile
31. awn	74. laws	117. sawn	160. snag	203. wiles
32. awnless	75. lea	118. saws	161. snags	204. win
33. awns	76. lean	119. sea	162. snail	205. wine
34. easing	77. leans	120. seal	163. snails	206. wineglass
35. egis	78. leasing	121. sealing	164. swag	207. wines
36. Gael	79. leg	122. seals	165. swage	208. wing
37. Gaels	80. legs	123. seas	166. swages	209. wingless
38. gain	81. lei	124. sen	167. swags	210. wings
39. gains	82. leis	125. sew	168. swain	211. wins
40. gal	83. lens	126. sewing	169. swains	212. wise
41. gale	84. less	127. sewings	170. swan	
42. gales	85. liane	128. sewn	171. swans	
43. gals	86. lianes	129. sews	172. swig	

#48

How many words can you make from these 9 letters? Every word must contain the letter "E". You can use only these 9 letters and a letter cannot be used more than once in any word (you may use 2 E's). It's possible to make one 9-letter word.

Score: 20 words or more – EXCELLENT

    15 words or more – VERY GOOD

    10 words or more - GOOD

Hint: don't forget the plural forms of words, for example dare is 1 word and dares is a 2nd word. It's possible to make 233 words of 4 or more letters. (See following page for answers).

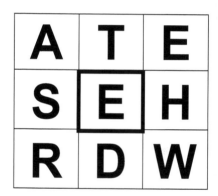

Answers:

1. adhere	48. hared	95. reed	142. swathed
2. adheres	49. hares	96. reeds	143. swather
3. Ares	50. haste	97. rest	144. swear
4. aster	51. hasted	98. rested	145. sweat
5. awed	52. hate	99. rhea	146. sweated
6. awes	53. hated	100. rheas	147. sweater
7. dare	54. hater	101. sadhe	148. Swede
8. dares	55. hates	102. sate	149. sweet
9. date	56. hatred	103. sated	150. tare
10. dater	57. hatreds	104. sawed	151. tared
11. dates	58. hawed	105. sawer	152. tares
12. dear	59. hawser	106. sear	153. tawed
13. dearest	60. head	107. seared	154. tawer
14. dears	61. headrest	108. seat	155. tear
15. dearth	62. heads	109. seated	156. teared
16. death	63. headset	110. sedate	157. tears
17. deaths	64. hear	111. seed	158. teas
18. deer	65. heard	112. seer	159. tease
19. desert	66. hears	113. sera	160. teased
20. deter	67. hearse	114. sere	161. teaser
21. deters	68. heart	115. sewed	162. teed
22. dews	69. hearted	116. sewer	163. tees
23. drew	70. hearts	117. shade	164. terse
24. eared	71. heat	118. shader	165. Tewa
25. ears	72. heated	119. share	166. Tewas
26. earth	73. heater	120. shared	167. thawed
27. earthed	74. heaters	121. shear	168. thee
28. earths	75. heats	122. sheared	169. there
29. ease	76. heed	123. shed	170. these
30. eased	77. heeds	124. sheer	171. thew
31. east	78. Hera	125. sheet	172. thews
32. Easter	79. herd	126. sherd	173. thread
33. eater	80. herds	127. shred	174. threads
34. eats	81. here	128. shrew	175. three
35. erase	82. hers	129. shrewd	176. threes
36. erased	83. hewed	130. stare	177. threw
37. Erse	84. hewer	131. stared	178. trade
38. ester	85. hews	132. stead	179. trades
39. Esther	86. rase	133. steed	180. trashed
40. ether	87. rased	134. steer	181. tread
41. ethers	88. rate	135. stere	182. treads
42. ewer	89. rated	136. stew	183. tree
43. ewers	90. rates	137. steward	184. treed
44. ewes	91. rawest	138. stewed	185. trees
45. hades	92. read	139. strew	186. tsade
46. hardest	93. reads	140. strewed	187. tweed
47. hare	94. reds	141. swathe	188. tweeds

189. wade
190. wader
191. waders
192. wades
193. ware
194. wared
195. wares
196. warted
197. washed
198. washer
199. waste
200. wasted
201. waster
202. water
203. watered
204. waters
205. watershed
206. wear
207. wears
208. weather
209. weathers
210. weds
211. weed
212. weeds
213. weer
214. weest
215. were
216. wert
217. west
218. wether
219. wethers
220. wets
221. wheat
222. where
223. whereas
224. whereat
225. whet
226. whets
227. wreath
228. wreathe
229. wreathed
230. wreathes
231. wreaths
232. wrest
233. wrested

#49

How many words can you make from these 9 letters? There is no letter which must be used in every word. You can only use these 9 letters and a letter cannot be used more than once in any word. It's possible to make one 9-letter word.

Score: 20 words or more – EXCELLENT

    15 words or more – VERY GOOD

    10 words or more - GOOD

Hint: don't forget the plural forms of words, for example ace is 1 word and aces is a 2nd word. It's possible to make 153 words of 3 or more letters. (See following page for answers).

E	Y	C
S	V	T
M	O	A

Answers:

1. ace	40. cot	79. move	118. tacos
2. aces	41. cote	80. moves	119. tame
3. acme	42. cotes	81. oat	120. tames
4. act	43. cots	82. oats	121. tea
5. acts	44. cove	83. octave	122. team
6. ascot	45. coves	84. ova	123. teams
7. ate	46. covet	85. ovate	124. teas
8. atom	47. covets	86. sac	125. toe
9. atoms	48. covey	87. same	126. toea
10. avo	49. coveys	88. sat	127. toes
11. avocet	50. coy	89. sate	128. tom
12. avocets	51. coyest	90. save	129. tome
13. avos	52. cyst	91. say	130. tomes
14. aye	53. east	92. scam	131. toms
15. ayes	54. easy	93. scat	132. toy
16. cam	55. eat	94. Scot	133. toys
17. came	56. eats	95. sea	134. vas
18. cameo	57. ems	96. seam	135. vase
19. cameos	58. eta	97. seamy	136. vasectomy
20. cams	59. mace	98. seat	137. vast
21. case	60. maces	99. sec	138. vat
22. cast	61. mascot	100. sect	139. vats
23. caste	62. mast	101. set	140. vest
24. cat	63. mat	102. smote	141. Vesta
25. cats	64. mate	103. some	142. vet
26. cave	65. mates	104. sot	143. veto
27. caves	66. mats	105. soy	144. vets
28. cay	67. may	106. stave	145. vote
29. coast	68. meat	107. stay	146. votes
30. coat	69. mesa	108. steam	147. yam
31. coats	70. met	109. steamy	148. yams
32. coma	71. moat	110. stem	149. yea
33. comas	72. moats	111. stoa	150. yeas
34. come	73. mosey	112. stoae	151. yeast
35. comes	74. most	113. stoma	152. yes
36. comet	75. mot	114. stove	153. yet
37. comets	76. mote	115. sty	
38. cost	77. motes	116. stye	
39. cosy	78. mots	117. taco	

#50

How many words can you make from these 9 letters? There is no letter which must be used in every word. You can only use these 9 letters and a letter cannot be used more than once in any word (you may use 2 I's). It's possible to make one 9-letter word.

Score: 20 words or more – EXCELLENT

    15 words or more – VERY GOOD

    10 words or more - GOOD

It's possible to make 161 words of 3 or more letters. (See following page for answers).

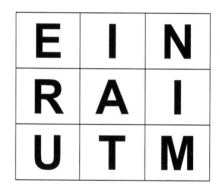

Answers: _____ _____ _____ _____

_____ _____ _____ _____

_____ _____ _____ _____

_____ _____ _____ _____

_____ _____ _____ _____

_____ _____ _____ _____

_____ _____ _____ _____

_____ _____ _____ _____

_____ _____ _____ _____

_____ _____ _____ _____

_____ _____ _____ _____

_____ _____ _____ _____

_____ _____ _____ _____

_____ _____ _____ _____

1. aim	42. mare	83. net	124. tare
2. Ainu	43. marine	84. nit	125. tarn
3. air	44. mart	85. niter	126. tau
4. airmen	45. marten	86. nitre	127. tea
5. airtime	46. martin	87. nut	128. team
6. amen	47. martini	88. nutria	129. tear
7. amine	48. mat	89. raiment	130. ten
8. amir	49. mate	90. rain	131. term
9. ant	50. mature	91. ram	132. termini
10. ante	51. mean	92. ramie	133. tern
11. anti	52. meant	93. ran	134. tie
12. are	53. meat	94. rani	135. tier
13. arm	54. men	95. rant	136. time
14. art	55. menu	96. rat	137. timer
15. arum	56. merit	97. rate	138. tin
16. ate	57. met	98. ream	139. tine
17. atrium	58. mien	99. rein	140. tinier
18. aunt	59. min	100. rem	141. tire
19. ear	60. mina	101. remain	142. train
20. earn	61. minaret	102. remit	143. tram
21. eat	62. mine	103. rent	144. trim
22. emir	63. mini	104. retain	145. trine
23. emit	64. miniature	105. retina	146. true
24. emu	65. mint	106. rim	147. tun
25. era	66. minter	107. rime	148. tuna
26. inert	67. minuet	108. rite	149. tune
27. inertia	68. minute	109. rue	150. tuner
28. inmate	69. minutia	110. ruin	151. turn
29. inter	70. minutiae	111. rum	152. unit
30. interim	71. mire	112. rumen	153. unite
31. Inuit	72. mite	113. rumina	154. untie
32. inure	73. miter	114. ruminate	155. urea
33. irate	74. mitre	115. run	156. uremia
34. ire	75. mute	116. rune	157. urinate
35. item	76. muter	117. runt	158. urine
36. main	77. nae	118. rut	159. urn
37. man	78. name	119. Tai	160. Ute
38. mane	79. namer	120. tame	161. uteri
39. manitu	80. nature	121. tamer	
40. manure	81. near	122. tan	
41. mar	82. neat	123. tar	

ABOUT THE AUTHOR

Daniel Wieczorek was born in 1947 in Ionia, Michigan. He graduated from the University of Michigan with a B.S. in Forestry in 1969. He moved to Oregon to work in the field of forestry in 1971. That was followed by a move to Alaska in 1975, where he continued his career in forestry. After about a 14 year career in forestry, Daniel decided to do something different and he served as a Peace Corps Volunteer in The Philippines from 1985 – 1987. Upon completion of his Peace Corps service he returned to Alaska, where he attended the University of Alaska – Fairbanks and received an M.B.A. in 1991. This was followed by a move to South Korea in 1992, where Daniel taught English to Korean people wishing to improve their English Language skills. Daniel's next stop was in New York City, where he worked as temporary staff at Deutsche Bank from 1998 – 2001. He left NYC in March 2001 and moved on to his present home in Mitaka City, Tokyo, Japan. He is teaching English in Japan and at this time he's been teaching as a career for about 17 years. He has been hiking, climbing and doing photography since he was about 12 years old.